At a Glance Map

The map below shows the regions that the guide is split into, and the page number where each region starts. A detailed map is on page 143.

Pg112 — NORTHUMBERLAND, DURHAM & HADRIAN'S WALL

Pg96 — NORTH WEST CITIES & LAKELAND

Pg84 — YORKSHIRE DALES, MOORS & COASTLINE

Pg72 — DERBYSHIRE DALES, PEAKS & STAFFORDSHIRE MOORLANDS

Pg60 — SHERWOOD FOREST & LINCOLNSHIRE WOLDS

Pg64 — STRATFORD & THE WELSH BORDERS

Pg52 — EAST ANGLIA, FENS & BEACHES

Pg120 — WELSH MOUNTAINS, MOORS & COASTLINE

Pg16 — LONDON

Pg24 — THE SOUTH WEST

Pg40 — HOME COUNTIES & THE SOUTH EAST COAST

Pg22 — THE ISLAND OF JERSEY

It's easy to book

To check availability and make a booking visit www.yha.org.uk or phone the contact centre on 0870 770 8868

C000101568

Ab...

2
3
4
6   What to expect in a Youth Hostel
8   Rent-a-Tipi
8   Camping
9   Camping barns
9   Bunkhouses
10   Escape to...
12   A place for people
14   Food

Regional entries

16   London
22   The Island of Jersey
24   The South West
40   Home Counties and the South East Coast
52   East Anglia, Fens and Beaches
60   Sherwood Forest and Lincolnshire Wolds
64   Stratford and the Welsh Borders
72   Derbyshire Dales, Peaks and Staffordshire Moorlands
84   Yorkshire Dales, Moors and Coastline.
96   North West Cities and Lakeland
112   Northumberland, Durham and Hadrian's Wall
120   Welsh Mountains, Moors and Coastline

References

136   FAQ
138   Index by type of location
140   Alphabetical index
143   Map
145   Symbols

YHA Ilam

We offer choice.

YHA Thameside, London

We're unique and that's what sets us apart. You'll stay in a mansion, a cottage, a lodge, somewhere modern and purpose built or in a converted mill. Each location is different and that's what makes us special.

YHA Snowdon Ranger

YHA Treyarnon Bay

YHA Clun Mill

Relax.

Times have changed. You don't have to share, do chores or stay out in the rain. Sit back and relax for as long as you like or explore the wide world outside day or night. It's up to you.

Canalside at YHA Manchester

YHA Exford

City, Coast or Countryside

The best of England and Wales. Whether you prefer busy cities with vibrant nightlife, splendid coastlines, beaches and cliffs, quiet market towns in outstanding countryside or remote wild places where we offer the only accommodation, YHA has it all.

What to expect in a Youth Hostel

Lounge at YHA Sherwood

We offer choice.

We offer more than a bunkroom, more than just bedrooms. We serve meals and you'll find a lounge to sit back and relax in comfort at most locations. There's usually a kitchen where you can prepare your own meals if you want to as well as a drying room, car park and secure cycle storage at many sites. Many have their own grounds or gardens, and some offer games rooms or TV lounges. And there's a friendly informal welcome everywhere.

Kitchen at YHA Lizard

Secure storage

YHA St Pancras, London

For more information visit www.yha.org.uk or call 0870 770 8868

Double room at YHA Hartington

Locks on all rooms

Quality and comfort.

Our accommodation is assessed by VisitBritain according to their National Quality Assurance Standards for Youth Hostels. The locations are assessed for both quality and facilities, including cleanliness, the friendliness and efficiency of staff, furnishings, decor and food.

The facilities are listed under each YHA entry and a key to these symbols is on the back cover flap - page 143.

★	Simple, practical, no frills
★★	Well presented and well run
★★★	Good level of quality and comfort
★★★★	Excellent standard throughout
★★★★★	Exceptional with a high standard throughout

Bunkhouses and Camping Barns are also assessed and although they are not given a star rating they must reach the VisitBritain minimum requirements.

Welsh guesthouses are awarded ◆ See www.visitwales.com for more details.

Rooms at all locations have either a personal safety lock or 24-hour key code. Our accommodation is open to all, but non-members will need to show identification when they check in.

Room sizes vary. Shared bunkrooms are standard, shared with others of the same sex. Children need to be over five to stay in shared bunkrooms, but private family rooms are increasingly available at many locations - shown by this symbol

Rent-A-Tipi

YHA Burley

Try camping with a difference and sleep under the stars in a handmade tipi created from an authentic native American design. Our high quality tents are surprisingly luxurious and comfortable as they come complete with carpets, airbeds and bedding and have a spacious living area - big enough to cope with six people. There's even a central heater to keep you warm on those chilly nights.

See symbol

from only

£60

per Tipi per night

Camping

Campers can take advantage of the superb locations of 35 YHA properties by pitching their tents in the grounds.

Those who stay are welcome to use the building's toilet, laundry and kitchen facilities as well as the lounge, games room and bathrooms.

Prices per person per night equate to half the normal adult overnight rate at that site.

See symbol

from only

£7

per person per night

For more information visit www.yha.org.uk or call 0870 770 8868

Camping Barns

YHA Abney

There are more than 30 Camping Barns in the YHA network owned and operated by farmers in fantastic rural locations. They provide great value and great fun.

Facilities vary from barn to barn, but typically offer sleeping platforms, spaces to prepare and eat food, cold running water, a flush toilet and parking. You'll need to bring a sleeping bag, torch, warm clothes and walking boots or wellies. You may also need cooking utensils, a camping stove and fuel.

from only

£5

per person per night

Bunkhouses

YHA's Bunkhouses provide a great budget option offering accommodation in spectacular rural locations at great value for money prices.

All are self-catering and must be booked in advance. You have to bring your own sleeping bag and bedrooms are mainly dormitory-style with bunk beds, although there are some private family rooms. All properties come with basic facilities including hot showers, drying room and self-catering kitchen.

YHA Portreath

from only

£10

per person per night

YHA All Stretton

Escape to...

Mansions, Lodges and Cottages. Superb, unique buildings for exclusive hire in great locations across England and Wales.

YHA Exeter

Flexibility.

Whether you're planning a break with family, friends, colleagues or an organised group - we've got over 100 properties that are perfect for any occasion. From a party of ten to a gathering of over one hundred you won't be disappointed by the sea views, mountain vistas, bustling towns and forest retreats that we have to offer.

With Escape to... you enjoy exclusive use of the property for the entire duration of your stay.

YHA Black Sail

For more information visit www.yha.org.uk or call 0870 770 8868

YHA Medway

YHA Shining Cliff

from only

£8

per person per night based on full occupancy

Choice.

All Escape to... venues have a self-catering kitchen, fully equipped with everything you might need including wine glasses and a corkscrew! Some provide a catering service, offering delicious breakfasts, picnic lunches and evening meals. A few may also be able to prepare celebratory meals for special occasions. Tell us in advance of any special dietary requirements and we can ensure there's a tasty meal to suit everyone.

See symbol **E2**

YHA Lee Valley

YHA Capel Curig

A Place for People

Accessibility.

Each new YHA is designed to offer wheelchair access and many have had induction loops and tactile signage installed. We are auditing our older buildings, using the National Accessible Scheme (NAS) criteria to determine what levels of access are required. YHA is a registered user of Typetalk. Registered assistance dogs are allowed at most YHAs. Our staff are also trained to meet the needs of every guest, ensuring that their stay with YHA is both enjoyable and memorable.

 NAS Mobility 1 Typically suitable for a person with sufficient mobility to climb a flight of steps.

 NAS Mobility 2 Typically suitable for a person with restricted walking ability and those that may need a wheelchair some of the time and can negotiate a maximum of three steps.

 NAS Mobility 3 Typically suitable for a person who depends on the use of a wheelchair and transfers unaided to and from the wheelchair in a seated position.

 NAS Visual 1 Minimum entry requirements to meet the National Accessible Standards for visually impaired guests.

 NAS Hearing 1 Minimum entry requirements to meet the National Accessible Standards for guests with hearing impairment, from mild hearing impairment to profoundly deaf.

Families

Stay in a family room for a special price with bunk beds, washbasin, bed linen and duvets included. Rooms are available for families with children aged three years or over - younger at some sites - ask when booking. Meals are usually available, with special menus for under 10s. En-suite facilities and double beds are sometimes an option. Come and go with your own key during the day to use the facilities, including the self-catering kitchen. If there are no family rooms at your chosen location, many sites can offer a bunkroom for your exclusive use each night.

Rooms from only

£32.50

per room per night

Family room at YHA Edale

Shared accommodation from only

£9.95

per person per night

Great Food Available.

We take pride in offering great British food, simply prepared with ingredients carefully selected from local producers. Compliment your meal with fantastic regional ales, international wines, beers, spirits, and Fair Trade tea and coffee. All enjoyed in comfortable, informal surroundings, and great value for money.

For information and to book visit **www.yha.org.uk** or call **0870 770 8868**

The Grain House café
YHA Bristol

The Big Blue café
at YHA Treyarnon

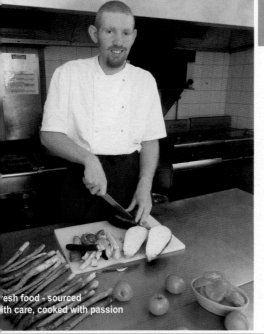

Fresh food - sourced
with care, cooked with passion

Food, Food, Food!

After a hard day's fun, kick back and enjoy a meal with friends at YHA. You'll always find great British food on offer and popular international favourites too. From a hearty breakfast, to a picnic lunch and home-cooked meals, YHA has a fantastic range of food to choose from. You won't escape the sticky toffee pudding, so give in and indulge yourselves. All washed down with the best of British and imported beverages.

 Food available   Café

 Licensed   Bar

 Self catering only

London

London, one of the world's biggest and best-known cities is a lively cosmopolitan metropolis that sits either side of the River Thames. Getting around is easy, forget the car and use the London Underground, buses, boats, and trains.

From museums to river trips and theatres to cinemas, you'll be glad of our warm welcome and comfortable beds at the end of a hectic day.

The London Eye

For information and to book visit **www.yha.org.uk** or call **0870 770 8868**

uthbank, London
w.britainonview.com

TOTTENHAM COURT
ROAD

WESTMINSTER
CCTV
Making our streets safer
TEL 020 7641 6511

73

yha ST. ...
INTERNATIONAL

LONDON
A-Z

Family Facilities

St Pancras   20
St Paul's   20
Thameside   21

For information and to book visit **www.yha.org.uk** or call **0870 770 8868**   17

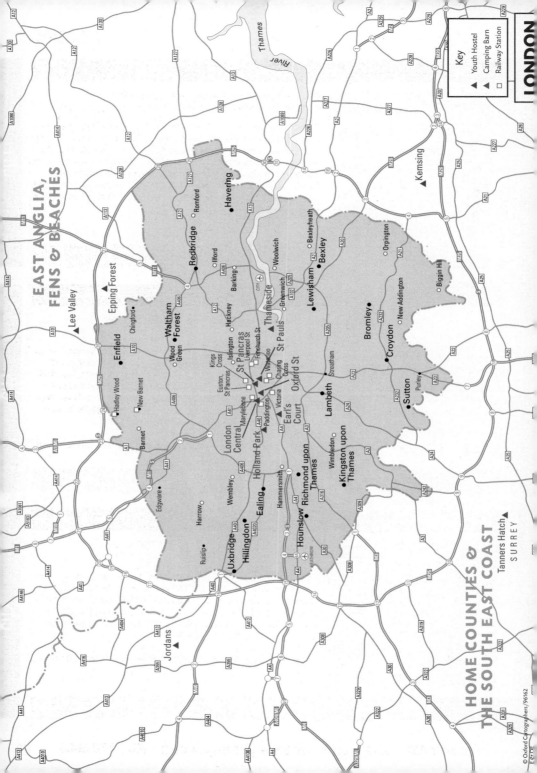

LONDON

Key
▲ Youth Hostel
▲ Camping Barn
□ Railway Station

EAST ANGLIA, FENS & BEACHES

HOME COUNTIES & THE SOUTH EAST COAST

River Thames

Thames

Lee Valley ▲
Epping Forest ▲
Chingford
Enfield ●
Wood Green ●
Waltham Forest ●
Hackney ○
Hadley Wood ●
New Barnet □
Barnet ○
Edgware ○
Wembley ○
Harrow ○
Ruislip ○
Uxbridge ●
Hillingdon ●
Ealing ●
Hammersmith ○
Hounslow ●
Richmond upon Thames ●
Wimbledon ○
Kingston upon Thames ●

London Central
Holland Park ▲
Marylebone
Paddington
Earl's Court
Euston, St Pancras
Kings Cross
Islington ○
St Pancras
Euston
Charing Cross
Victoria
Oxford St
Waterloo
Liverpool St
Fenchurch St
St Pauls ▲
Lambeth ●
Streatham
Thameside ▲

Redbridge ●
Romford ○
Havering ●
Ilford ○
Barking ○
Woolwich ●
Greenwich ○
Bexleyheath ○
Bexley ●
Lewisham ●
Orpington ○
New Addington ○
Biggin Hill ○
Bromley ●
Croydon ●
Purley ○
Sutton ●

Kemsing ▲

Jordans ▲

Tanners Hatch ▲
SURREY

© Oxford Cartographers/96162

Central

New YHA for 2007!

Bolsover Street, City of Westminster, London W1
Details to be confirmed - visit the website for more information

Scheduled to open in 2007, this brand new flagship site offers up-to-the-minute facilities in the heart of London's West End. It's just a few minutes walk from the shopping mecca of Oxford Street and its excellent position and superb public transport links make it the perfect base for exploring the capital's many attractions. It meets the needs of all visitors, boasting a large reception area, coffee shop, residents' bar and restaurant and travel desk as well as a variety of smaller rooms - most of which will be en-suite.

CITY

Earl's Court ★★★

38 Bolton Gardens, Earl's Court, London SW5 0AQ
Tel: 0870 770 5804

Cosmopolitan Earl's Court is the place to meet and make friends. The nearby Olympia and Earl's Court exhibition centres host live gigs and international events. Hyde Park, The Natural History Museum, Victoria & Albert Museum and Science Museum are all nearby. Eating is easy - there's a large self-catering kitchen here and a great choice of lively bars, pubs and restaurants nearby. In summer, our courtyard garden is often filled with people chilling after a hectic day or night out.

Accommodation: 170 beds: mainly 4-6-bed rooms, plus some 2-, 3-bed options.

CITY

          24 hours

Holland Park ★★★ A

Holland Walk, Kensington, London W8 7QU
Tel: 0870 770 5866

In the middle of a park this Jacobean mansion is ideal for a peaceful stay in the heart of London. Near to the Victoria & Albert, Natural History and Science Museums, a short bus or tube ride will take you to Kensington Palace and the BBC Television Centre, which does tours. Breakfast is included. Try our excellent food served in the restaurant, opening onto private gardens and an ornamental pond.

Accommodation: 200 beds: a few 6-8-bed rooms, mostly 12-20-bed rooms.

CITY

            24 hours

London

Oxford Street ★★ A

14 Noel Street, London W1F 8GJ
Tel: 0870 770 5984

A shopper's paradise with nightlife right on the doorstep too, YHA Oxford Street neighbours some of Britain's biggest high street names. We're handy for London's theatres, the internationally acclaimed art exhibitions of Burlington House and the British Museum's vast collection of historic and archaeological artifacts. If you've shopped until you're ready to drop, stroll into China Town for some Dim Sum or into one of the many cosmopolitan cafés, ethnic restaurants and pubs in Soho.

Accommodation: 75 beds: all 2-, 3- and 4-bed rooms.

      24 hours

St Pancras ★★★★ A

79-81 Euston Road, London NW1 2QE
Tel: 0870 770 6044

Opposite St Pancras, minutes from King's Cross and Euston rail and tube stations, our modern facilities make an ideal hub for people on the move and great for exploring London. Two tube stops from Camden Town's vibrant weekend craft markets and the famous London Zoo you can also immerse yourself in the British Library (opposite) or discover the London Canal Museum, in a former ice warehouse where two underground 'ice wells' are still preserved. Eat in at our excellent restaurant.

Accommodation: 152 beds: 10x2-, 1x3-, 18x4-, 3x5-bed rooms, plus 7x6-bed rooms, mostly en-suite.

             24 hours

St Paul's ★★★ A

36 Carter Lane, London EC4V 5AB
Tel: 0870 770 5764

This former school overlooked by St Paul's Cathedral in the city's business district is a quieter base for exploring the capital, with the West End minutes away by excellent transport links. The Barbican Centre, also home to the Museum of London, offers free lunchtime concerts nearby. A stroll over the Millennium Bridge across the River Thames is the Tate Modern Gallery and the Globe Shakespeare Centre or for a real taste of city-life, sample a local Champagne and Oyster Bar.

Accommodation: 190 beds: several 1-, 2- and 3-bed rooms, mainly 4-8-bed, plus 1x10-bed and 1x11-bed options.

             24 hours

For information and to book visit **www.yha.org.uk** or call **0870 770 8868**

London

Thameside

20 Salter Road, Rotherhithe, London SE16 5PR
Tel: 0870 770 6010

A modern, purpose-built base for exploring the capital. Attractions like the Tower of London, Tower Bridge and the London Dungeon are a short walk away with excellent transport links to the many sights of the city centre. Choose from the Quays' café-bar with pastries, snacks or a delicious latte and 'The Traders Galley' restaurant with a good varied menu.

Accommodation: 320 beds: some 2-, 3-, 4-, 5- and 6-bed rooms, plus 3x10-bed rooms, all en-suite.

CITY

 24 hours

YHA Travel Desk

Port Douglas - Australia

Chicago

YHA Oxford

To book contact the YHA Travel desk at travel@yha.org.uk or tel: +44 (0)207 341 7552.

YHA Earl's Court is the first YHA to open a dedicated travel desk to offer both UK & International packages to our members and visitors from other associations. The International products include many packages from other IYHF associations throughout the world.

travel@yha.org.uk or Telephone: +44 (0)207 341 7552

The Island of Jersey

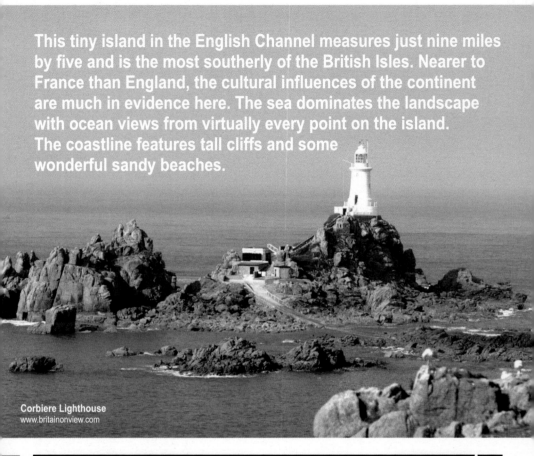

This tiny island in the English Channel measures just nine miles by five and is the most southerly of the British Isles. Nearer to France than England, the cultural influences of the continent are much in evidence here. The sea dominates the landscape with ocean views from virtually every point on the island. The coastline features tall cliffs and some wonderful sandy beaches.

Corbiere Lighthouse
www.britainonview.com

COAST

| Jersey | Star rating - awaiting clasification | D |

Haut de la Garenne, La rue de la Poucle et des Quatre Chemins, St Martin, Jersey JE3 6DU
Tel: 0870 770 6130

Mild climate and sandy beaches make Jersey popular with holidaymakers of all ages. This former Victorian school is on the island's popular east coast where you'll find beaches, opportunities for watersports and low level walks with sea views. The majestic Mont Orgueil Castle, a maritime centre and Jersey Zoo are close by. Take a day trip to France or discover the island's chequered history at the the German Underground Hospital.

Accommodation: 105 beds: 5x2-, 1x3-, 6x4-, 3x6-, 4x8+ bedded rooms, some with en-suite.

E2   BBQ

7.00-10.00am
5.00-11.00pm

For information and to book visit **www.yha.org.uk** or call **0870 770 8868**

YHA Membership

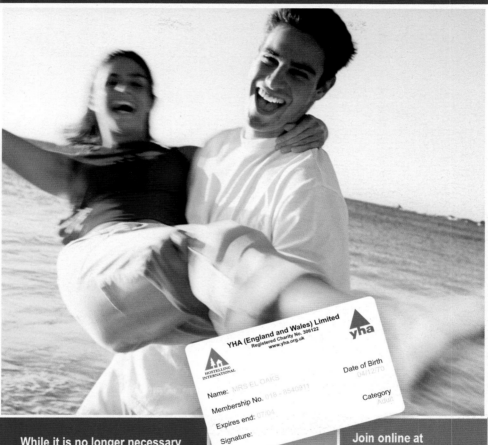

YHA (England and Wales) Limited
Registered Charity No. 306122
www.yha.org.uk

HOSTELLING INTERNATIONAL

Name: MRS EL OAKS

Membership No. 018 – 8540911

Expires end: 07/04

Signature:

Date of Birth
04/12/70

Category
Adult

While it is no longer necessary to be a member to stay with YHA, membership is great value and you pay less for your overnight stays.

If you join as an individual or family member, you can get cheaper membership by paying by Direct Debit. If you are U26 a two or three year membership offers better value. We also offer life membership.

Join online at www.yha.org.uk or call: 0870 770 8868 with your credit/debit card details.

The South West

In South West England, the sea is never far away and the stunning coastline and beaches have made this area one of the UK's most popular holiday destinations.

It's easy to avoid the crowds; walk the South West Coastal Path, lose yourself on Dartmoor or Exmoor or just flop with a good book on one of the many secret hidden coves.

Housel Bay and Lizard Lighthouse, Cornwall
www.britainonview.com

For information and to book visit **www.yha.org.uk** or call **0870 770 8868**

Stonehenge, Wiltshire
britainonview / Martin Brent

Bath

Clifton Suspension Bridge
britainonview / Pawel Libera

Family Facilities

Bath	27	Lulworth	32
Beer	27	Lynton	32
Bellever	27	Minehead	32
Boscastle	28	Okehampton	33
Boswinger	28	Portland	34
Bristol	28	River Dart	34
Cheddar	29	Salcombe	35
Cholderton	29	Salisbury	35
Coverack	29	Slimbridge	35
Exeter	30	Stow	36
Exford	30	Street	36
Golant	30	Swanage	37
Litton	31	Treyarnon	37
Lizard	31		

For information and to book visit **www.yha.org.uk** or call **0870 770 8868**

THE SOUTH WEST

Key

▲ Youth Hostel
▲ Bunk House
▲ Camping Barn
▲ Guest House
□ Railway Station

© Oxford Cartographers/96162
E & OE

CITY

Bath

 D
★★★

Bathwick Hill, Bath BA2 6JZ
Tel: 0870 770 5688

A beautiful Italianate mansion and annexe in private gardens, YHA Bath offers a comfortable base for exploring this World Heritage City famous for its Roman heritage and Georgian architecture. Literally buzzing with cosmopolitan energy, Bath is home to all kinds of activities and attractions like the Roman Baths, Number One Royal Crescent and the Art Gallery. Eat in and enjoy great home cooking or sample the many pubs, restaurants and cafes in the city.

Accommodation: 121 beds: 5x2-, 11x4-, 3x5-, 4x6-, 1x8- and 2x10-bed rooms.

            24 hours

Beer

★★★ C

Bovey Combe, Beer, Seaton, Devon EX12 3LL
Tel: 0870 770 5690

A spacious country house, once a smuggler's haunt, YHA Beer sits in large grounds on the edge of this quaint fishing village. It's great for families or people just looking to relax and unwind. Follow the South West Coast Path to the dramatic headlands to the west or visit the Pecorama Pleasure Gardens - a magnet for children, with pony rides and a miniature railway. Fresh fish is often on the menu here and trips can be arranged for you to catch your supper!

Accommodation: 43 beds: 3x4-, 3x5-, 1x6- and 1x10-bed rooms.

              8.00-10.00am 5.00-10.00pm

COSTAL

Bellever

  C
★★

Bellever, Postbridge, Devon PL20 6TU
Tel: 0870 770 5692

YHA Bellever is a former Duchy farm with a wildlife area full of interesting flora and fauna. It's located near Postbridge on Dartmoor, Southern Britain's largest wilderness. The nearby East Dart River, Bellever Forest and Tor are ideal for family rambles. Children also love the Miniature Pony Centre where they can ride and groom the ponies. Great home cooked food using local ingredients is available from the hostel.

Accommodation: 38 beds: 3x6-, 3x4- and 1x8-bed rooms.

        8.00-10.00am 5.00-10.30pm

COUNTRYSIDE

The South West

Boscastle Harbour

Palace Stables, Boscastle, Cornwall PL35 0HD
Tel: 0870 770 5710

Boscastle sits in a steep-sided valley on the rugged north Cornwall coast. A flash flood in 2004 severely damaged this National Trust-owned harbour-side building, but it is now open again and is better than ever following a massive refurbishment scheme. It's an ideal spot to sit and watch this pretty, bustling fishing village come to life during the day and return to a sleepier pace in the evenings. You'll also find excellent surfing and sailing and miles of coastal footpaths to explore.

Accommodation: 24 beds: 2x6-, 1x5-, 1x4- 1x3- bed rooms.

  E2   8.00-10.00am 5.00-10.00pm

Boswinger

Boswinger, Gorran, St Austell, Cornwall PL26 6LL
Tel: 0870 770 5712

Offering excellent sea views, YHA Boswinger is a huddle of cosy farm buildings built around a courtyard. It's ideal for families or small groups wishing to explore south Cornwall's stunning unspoilt beaches and coastal footpath. Visit the nearby Lost Gardens of Heligan, voted the nation's favourite garden, or the world famous Eden Project. In the evening, take a relaxing sunset stroll to the nearby Hemmick Beach, or meet the locals in the pub at Gorran.

Accommodation: 40 beds: 3x2-, 4x4- and 3x6-bed rooms.

  E2 24 BBQ   8.00-10.00am 5.00- 9.30pm

Bristol

14 Narrow Quay, Bristol BS1 4QA
Tel: 0870 770 5726

This imaginatively converted harbour-side warehouse is an ideal base for families, individuals and groups to seek out the dozens of places of interest in this historic, vibrant city. Bristol Zoo is well worth a visit as is Brunel's first ocean-going, propeller-driven ship, the SS Great Britain. A drive over the great man's suspension bridge is also a must. Watch the world go by from our relaxing cafe where good food is guaranteed or chill out in the many bars and cafes around the dock.

Accommodation: 99 beds: mostly 4-bed rooms, plus 2x2-, 2x1-, 3x6- 1x8-and 1x3-.

 24   24 hours

For information and to book visit **www.yha.org.uk** or call **0870 770 8868**

Cheddar ★★★ B

Hillfield, Cheddar, Somerset BS27 3HN
Tel: 0870 770 5760

This large Victorian house in Cheddar village is just a mile away from the famous gorge where the highest limestone cliffs in the UK can be found. They provide a wonderful adventure playground for families and walkers as do the nearby Mendips and Somerset Levels. Below the ground are Cheddar's incredible caves, including Wookey Hole. The seaside resort of Weston-super-Mare is also close by. Meals here are very popular or there are plenty of pubs in the village.

Accommodation: 45 beds: 3x2-, 5x4-, 1x5-, 1x6- and 1x8-bed rooms.

7.30-10.00am
5.00-10.30pm

COUNTRYSIDE

Cholderton A

Cholderton Rare Breeds Farm, Amesbury Road, Cholderton, Wiltshire SP4 0EW
Tel: 0870 770 6134

YHA Cholderton is part of a working Rare Breeds farm and guests can meet fellow residents such as pygmy goats, piglets and lambs. On the edge of Cholderton Village, the World Heritage Sites at Stonehenge and Woodhenge are very close by. Nearby Middle Wallop is home to the Museum of Army Flying while the Hawk Conservancy Centre at Andover offers flying displays of a different kind. There's a café bar on-site and pubs nearby.

Accommodation: 20 beds: 1x2-, 2x3 and 2x6-bed rooms.

8.00am -
8.00pm

COUNTRYSIDE

Coverack ★★★ C

Great for sea views!

Parc Behan, School Hill, Coverack, Helston, Cornwall TR12 6SA
Tel: 0870 770 5780

This converted Victorian country house enjoys panoramic views of dramatic cliffs and deserted coves. The South West Coast Path passes very close to the property's extensive grounds. The pretty fishing village of Coverack is not as well-known as some other Cornish locations, consequently, walkers, anglers and water-sports enthusiasts can enjoy their pursuits without the crowds. Tuck into home-cooked food, using fruit and vegetables grown in our own garden.

Accommodation: 35 beds: 1x3-, 4x4- and 2x8-bed rooms.

8.00-10.00am
5.00-10.00pm

COAST

The South West

Exeter  ★★★ B

Mount Wear House, 47 Countess Wear Road, Exeter, Devon EX2 6LR
Tel: 0870 770 5826

This spacious 17th century house is tucked away on the edge of the city, close to the River Exe and the Ship Canal in private, tranquil grounds. Exeter is surrounded by beautiful countryside and is just a few miles from the sea. The city centre is a 10-minute bus ride away and is home to the Royal Albert Memorial Museum and numerous catacombs, museums, galleries and shops. It's an area famed for its food and drink and you'll find some good examples in our restaurant.

Accommodation: 66 beds: 1x2-, 6x4-, 2x5-, 1x6- and 3x8-bed rooms.

                  **8.00-10.00am / 5.00-10.00pm**

Exford ★★★ C

Exe Mead, Exford, Minehead, Somerset TA24 7PU
Tel: 0870 770 5828

In the pretty Somerset village of Exford, this large Victorian house stands in its own grounds by the River Exe in the heart of Exmoor National Park. It is a good base for walking and riding; explore the open hills and wooded valleys of this beautiful area. For the less energetic, Dunster - with its castle, gardens and working water mill - is only about 30 minutes away by road. Pack buckets and spades too for a trip to Minehead. Local food is a speciality at the hostel and there's an inn nearby.

Accommodation: 51 beds: some 2x2-bed rooms, mostly 4-6-bed options (3 en-suite).

                  8.00-10.00am / 5.00-10.00pm

Golant ★★★ C

Penquite House, Golant, Fowey, Cornwall PL23 1LA
Tel: 0870 770 5832

In private grounds overlooking the Fowey Estuary, with 14 acres of woodland to explore, this former private Georgian residence is a really relaxing get-away and is perfect for children. It's close to Bodmin Moor, with its numerous hiking and walking trails, prehistoric megaliths, stone circles and burial mounds, the Eden Project at Bodelva the Bodmin & Wenford steam railway. Fresh fish predictably features heavily on an excellent menu and there is a pub in the village.

Accommodation: 94 beds: 1x2-, 4x4-, 7x6-bed rooms, plus two larger dormitories.

                 7.30-10.00am / 5.00-10.30pm

For information and to book visit **www.yha.org.uk** or call **0870 770 8868**

Lands End **D**

Letcha Vean, St Just-in-Penwith, Penzance, Cornwall TR19 7NT
Tel: 0870 770 5906

YHA Land's End looks across this dramatic and rugged coastline and many rooms have sea views. The South West Coast Path is just a few minutes walk away and this location is a magnet for birdwatchers. The hostel is only four miles from the beautiful swimming and surfing beach at Sennen, and close to Lands End airfield for flights to the Isles of Scilly. Close by is the Levant Beam Engine-House and Geevor Tin Mine. The sunsets are magnificent, the food is excellent and if you fancy heading out at night, there are several pubs in nearby St Just (one mile).

Accommodation: 36 beds: 2x2-, 1x3-, 3x4-, 1x5- and 2x6-bed rooms.

 8.30-10.00am 5.00-10.00pm

COAST

Litton Cheney ★★★ **B**

Litton Cheney, Dorchester, Dorset DT2 9AT
To book more than 7 days ahead Tel: 0870 770 8868 Tel: 0870 770 5922

In an Area of Outstanding Natural Beauty, the Dorset village of Litton Cheney is surrounded by countryside that longs to be explored. Stay in this comfortable Dutch barn, close to the stunning Chesil Beach and Abbotsbury with its swannery, abbey and sub-tropical gardens. Near Lyme Regis in the heart of the Jurassic Coast World Heritage Site - great for fossil hunting, Hardy's Dorset, Bridport and West Bay. It's self-catering only but there are pubs close by if needed!

Accommodation: 22 beds: 2x2-, 3x4- and 1x6-bed rooms.

 7.30-10.00am 5.00-10.30pm

COUNTRYSIDE

Lizard ★★★★★ **A**

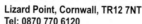

Lizard Point, Cornwall, TR12 7NT
Tel: 0870 770 6120

This stunning former Victorian hotel is practically the southernmost building in Britain and its unique location takes your breath away. It has lots of double rooms with tremendous sea views, but you'll need to book early. Great for coastal walks and beachcombing, there's also the Goonhilly Satellite Earth Station or the Flambards Experience with a recreated Victorian village if the weather's bad. It's self-catering only but there's a pub and restaurant in Lizard village half a mile away.

Accommodation: 30 beds: 2x3- (en-suite, suitable for wheelchairs), 2x4- 2x5- and 1x6-bed rooms.

 8.00-10.00am 5.00-10.30pm

COAST

The South West

Lulworth Cove ★★ C

School Lane, West Lulworth, Wareham, Dorset BH20 5SA
Tel: 0870 770 5940

This single-storey timber property is on the edge of the tranquil fishing village of West Lulworth. Surrounded by fields and wonderful views of the Dorset hills, it's a mile's walk to the oyster-shaped Lulworth Cove. As the South West Coastal Path passes close by, this is a great retreat for walkers and families. Durdle Door has a lovely beach and the Tank Museum at Bovington and Monkey World are also close. The daily menu is excellent or visit nearby pubs and restaurants.

Accommodation: 34 beds: 3x4-, 2x5 and 2x6-bed rooms.

   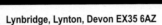

7.30-10.00am
5.00-10.30pm

Lynton ★★★ C

Lynbridge, Lynton, Devon EX35 6AZ
Tel: 0870 770 5942

Connected by a water-powered cliff railway, Lynton and Lynmouth were dubbed 'Little Switzerland' by the Victorians. YHA Lynton is a former country hotel on the side of a deep wooded gorge and offers easy access to both villages. Visit Lundy, an unspoilt, tranquil island or take a walk in the stunning 'Valley of the Rocks'. Kids love Dinosaur Park and the Big Sheep Working Farm. The restaurant menu features home-made meals using local, fresh and organic ingredients.

Accommodation: 36 beds: 2x2-, 2x4- and 4x6-bed rooms.

8.00-10.00am
5.00-10.00pm

Minehead ★★★ E

Alcombe Combe, Minehead, Somerset TA24 6EW
Tel: 0870 770 5968

If you've ever wondered which view was the inspiration behind the hymn 'All things bright and beautiful', the answer lies at YHA Minehead. This attractive country house sits high in Somerset's Exmoor hills and is a great place to relax away from it all, enjoy a private get-together or take an activity break. You can see badgers and red deer in the garden or walk to the sandy beach just two miles away. Delicious meals using local produce are available on-site.

Accommodation: 35 beds: 1x3-, 5x4- and 2x6-bed rooms.

8.15-10.00am
5.00-10.30pm

For information and to book visit **www.yha.org.uk** or call **0870 770 8868**

Okehampton A

Klondyke Road, Okehampton EX20 1EW
Tel: 0870 770 5978

This former Victorian railway shed is now a licensed adventure centre offering bright modern accommodation and serious amounts of fun and excitement. Try climbing, gorge scrambling, pony trekking, archery, treasure hunts and lots more or opt for a more relaxed pace by exploring Dartmoor on foot. The National Trust Lydford Gorge and the 90ft tall Whitelady Waterfall are close by as are the Devil's Cauldron Whirlpools. Eat in or out, at a choice of venues nearby.

Accommodation: 124 beds: all 2-, 4-, 6-bed rooms.

8.00-10.00am
5.00-9.00pm

COUNTRYSIDE

Penzance C

Castle Horneck, Alverton, Penzance, Cornwall TR20 8TF
Tel: 0870 770 5992

Set in landscaped gardens, this Georgian manor has wonderful views across Mounts Bay and The Lizard peninsula. Art lovers can visit the Tate Gallery at St Ives and there are also many private galleries exhibiting local work. Take a bus trip from the door to some of the most beautiful beaches and coastal walks in Britain, or to see a performance at the cliff-top Minack Theatre. Pizza and clotted ice cream are house specials in our restaurant or head out for a night out in Penzance's many pubs and restaurants.

Accommodation: 80 beds: mostly 4-10-bed rooms.

8.00-10.00am
5.00-10.30pm

COAST

Perranporth ★★ B

Droskyn Point, Perranporth, Cornwall TR6 0GS
Tel: 0870 770 5994

This former Coastguard Station overlooks three miles of beaches from the top of north Cornwall's rugged cliffs. Pounded by Atlantic rollers, the immaculately clean Perran Bay is as good for surfing as nearby Newquay but much less busy. Braver souls can also try hang-gliding, para-sailing and paragliding. Look for seals and dolphins at the St Agnes Marine Conservation Area and see the World in Miniature at Goonhaven. It's self-catering only but nearby pubs serve food.

Accommodation: 24 beds: 2x4- and 2x8-bed rooms.

8.00-10.00am
5.00-10.00pm

COAST

For information and to book visit **www.yha.org.uk** or call **0870 770 8868**   33

The South West

Portland C

Hardy House, Castle Road, Portland, Dorset DT5 1AU
Tel: 0870 770 6000

This early Edwardian building on the edge of the isle once belonged to the First Admiral and offers extensive views over Lyme Bay. It provides a great base for discovering Portland's heritage, including the Portland castle and lighthouse. Visit Chesil Beach or nearby Weymouth with its award-winning beaches, or make the most of the area's 185 million year history with a Fossil Forage. Breakfast is included and once you've sampled our home cooking you won't resist our dinner menu.

Accommodation: 28 beds: 1x4- and 4x6-bed rooms.

        8.30-10.00am 5.00-9.30pm

Quantock Hills F

Sevenacres, Holford, Bridgwater, Somerset TA5 1SQ
Tel: 0870 770 6006

Set high in the Quantock Hills, this traditional country house enjoys superb views towards the Bristol Channel. It's located on the Coleridge Way in ideal walking country and there's a path to Kilve Beach to hunt for fossils; also the Quantocks are a favourite spot for mountain bikers. Nearby the West Somerset Steam Railway covers 20 miles of glorious Somerset countryside. On rainy days children love a trip to see the animals at Tropiquaria in Washford Cross. YHA Quantock Hills is self-catering only or there's food on offer in the local pub.

Accommodation: 24 beds: 1x2-, 1x4- and 3x6-bed rooms.

         8.00-10.00am 5.00-10.00pm

River Dart E

Galmpton, Brixham, Devon TQ5 0ET
Tel: 0870 770 5962

Occupying a commanding position overlooking the Dart, this Victorian mansion is ideal for exploring the English Riviera. Children love to watch the Paignton to Kingswear steam train chuff past the front door and you can also learn to sail and dive. Nearby Brixham is a fishing port where you can buy the day's catch on the harbour-side, while Paignton Zoo, the local beaches and Dartmoor all make great days out. Home-cooked meals and open fires await back at base.

Accommodation: 70 beds: all 4-, 5-, 6-, 8- and 12-bed rooms.

          8.30-10.00am 5.00-9.30pm

For information and to book visit **www.yha.org.uk** or call **0870 770 8868**

Salcombe   C

Sharpitor, Salcombe, Devon TQ8 8LW
Tel: 0870 770 6016

Salcombe is one of the best-known sailing centres in the UK, but anyone can enjoy a stay at this Edwardian National Trust property. Sitting in six acres of semi-tropical gardens, YHA Salcombe is also a haven for both watersports and beach lovers. It's surrounded by rugged coastal paths and secluded sandy coves so is also great for walking. We serve good local food, beers and cider in our restaurant or a wide selection of pubs and cafes in the town. Note - no daytime parking near the property.

Accommodation: 52 beds: 1x2-, 5x4-, 1x6-, 1x7-, 1x8- and 1x9-bed rooms.

COAST

7.00-10.00am
5.00-10.00pm

Salisbury ★★★ B

Milford Hill, Salisbury, Wiltshire SP1 2QW
Tel: 0870 770 6018

A secluded villa, set in private grounds and within easy walking distance of the famous cathedral and city centre. This area has many ancient sites including the impressive Roman villa at Rockbourne and the Iron Age Hill-fort at Old Sarum. See the regimental badges of Fovant carved into the chalk downs, or visit the Dorset Heavy Horse Centre. Evening meals are provided to pre-booked groups only but meals are available in the city centre.

Accommodation: 70 beds. Main house, 50 beds: 1x1-, 1x2-, 3x4-bed rooms, plus larger rooms; Lodge: 2x3-, 4x4-bed rooms.

COUNTRYSIDE

7.30am -
11.00pm

Slimbridge ★★★ F

Shepherd's Patch, Slimbridge, Gloucestershire GL2 7BP
Tel: 0870 770 6036

In addition to the comfortable rooms, this modern facility has an observation lounge for birdwatchers who come to visit the Wildfowl and Wetlands Trust's centre nearby. For walkers, the Severn Way passes by the door and the Cotswold Way is four miles away. Nearby Berkeley Castle is one of the best-preserved family seats in the country and the award-winning National Waterways Museum is at Gloucester docks. Excellent home cooked food made from local produce is available.

Accommodation: 56 beds: 5x2-, 5x4-8- and 1x10-bed rooms.

COUNTRYSIDE

8.00-10.00am
5.00-10.30pm

The South West

St Briavels Castle

St Briavels, Lydney, Gloucestershire GL15 6RG
Tel: 0870 770 6040

A unique chance to stay in a Norman castle complete with moat is offered at this English Heritage-owned property. Built as a hunting lodge for King John in 1205, its towers were added in 1293 as part of the 'Ring of Stone' around Wales. It hosts frequent medieval banquets in the summer evenings and is a perfect base for exploring the Royal Forest of Dean and the Wye Valley on foot or by cycle. There's a delicious menu on offer in the evenings and an inn next door.

Accommodation: 70 beds: 1x4-, 2x6- and 2x8-bed rooms, plus 3 larger rooms.

8.00-10.00am
5.00-10.30pm

Stow-on-the-Wold

The Square, Stow-on-the-Wold, Gloucestershire GL54 1AF
Tel: 0870 770 6050

This Grade II listed 17th Century town house is in the centre of the historic market town of Stow-on-the-Wold. It has lots of smaller en-suite rooms, which make it an ideal base for families and there's a play area as well as picnic tables in the garden. There are shops, pubs and cafes in town while a visit to nearby Moreton-in-Marsh on market day is a real treat. Four miles to the south Bourton-on-the-Water has a host of attractions. Excellent home-cooked meals are available.

Accommodation: 48 beds: 1x1-, 2x4-, 4x6-, 1x7- and 1x8- bed rooms, most en-suite.

8.00-10.00am
5.00-10.00pm

Street

The Chalet, Ivythorn Hill, Street, Somerset BA16 0TZ
Tel: 0870 770 6056

This Swiss-style chalet is surrounded by National Trust land and offers a quiet retreat with many rooms ideal for families. Overlooking Glastonbury Tor, it is within easy reach of the Mendip Hills, Somerset Levels, Polden Hills and mystical Glastonbury famed for its now legendary music festival. Street is home to Clark's shoes and there are bargain shoe shops galore as well as a free Shoe Museum. The site is self-catering only but the Wessex Hotel in the village serves food.

Accommodation: 28 beds: 2x3-, 4x4- and 1x6-bed rooms.

8.30-10.00am
5.00-11.00pm

For information and to book visit **www.yha.org.uk** or call **0870 770 8868**

Swanage C

Cluny, Cluny Crescent, Swanage, Dorset BH19 2BS
Tel: 0870 770 6058

An elegant Victorian townhouse offering fine views across Swanage Bay and just minutes from a safe, sandy 'Blue Flag' beach. It generally caters for school groups during the week and individuals and families at weekends and holidays. Guests can explore Swanage's town trails or the 95 miles stretch of Jurassic Coast, where children will love searching for dinosaur footprints at Worbarrow Bay or making a few of their own on the many beaches close by. Excellent meals served in-house.

Accommodation: 100 beds in small bedrooms.

COAST

              7.15am - 10.30pm

Tintagel  B

Dunderhole Point, Tintagel, Cornwall PL34 0DW
Tel: 0870 770 6068

Tintagel is an isolated, spectacular and atmospheric place where the legend of King Arthur hangs in the air. Our location offers stunning coastal views over Dunderhole Point and is ideal for those wanting to leave civilisation behind. Visit King Arthur's Great Hall, where 72 stained glass windows depict scenes from the legends, or take the precarious descent to Tintagel Cove to visit Merlin's Cave. This self-catering property is down a rough unlit track so take food, and a torch!

Accommodation: 22 beds, 1x2-, 2x4- and 2x6-bed rooms.

COAST

          8.00-10.00am 5.00-10.00pm

Treyarnon Bay A

Tregonnan, Treyarnon, Padstow, Cornwall PL28 8JR
Tel: 0870 770 6076

Surf, sand and romantic sunsets in summer, wild storms and log fires in winter - YHA Treyarnon has got it all. On the coastal path above a perfect sandy beach on the north Cornwall coast, it sits on a beach edge between Padstow and Porthcothan. You'll find a surf school, cycle hire and its own natural swimming pool. Padstow is just three miles away and the Eden Project is a half hour drive. Don't miss the home-cooked local produce on offer in our sea view dining room and bar.

Accommodation: 70 beds: 5x3-bed, 3x5-bed rooms, 4x4- and 4x6-bed rooms. Many rooms en-suite.

COAST

               8.00-10.00am 5.00-11.00pm

The South West

Clyffe Pypard `D`

The Goddard Arms, Wood Street, Clyffe Pypard, Near
Wootton Bassett, Wiltshire SN4 7PY
Tel: 01793 731386

Friendly bunkhouse offers comfortable accommodation and serves
real ale and home cooked food in one of the oldest pubs in
Wiltshire. Set in the village of Clyffe Pypard in a conservation area
close to the Ridgeway, it's ideally situated for walkers and cyclists
wanting to explore the Ridgeway footpath, Wiltshire Cycle Way, the
White Horse, Avebury and Silbury Hills. Showers are metered.

Portreath `A`

Nance Farm, Illogan, Redruth, Cornwall TR16 4QX
Tel: 01209 842244

Newly converted barn on working farm in the grounds of a Grade II
listed former manor house. Explore the grounds which are home
to an Iron Age round, ponds and a wooded valley trail to Portreath
Beach. Use it as a base for exploring Cornwall's many attractions.
Cooked breakfast available on request.

Chenson `X`

Booking: 0870 770 8868
Arrival number: 01363 83236

This cob and timber barn, formerly used for cider pressing, is on a
working farm in the beautiful Taw Valley. It is half mile from the
Tarka Trail, close to the Forestry Commission's Eggesford Forest
with many walks and mountain bike routes, and five miles from the
Two Moors Way. Facilities include two separate sleeping areas
upstairs, cooking facilities and sitting area downstairs. Breakfast
and cream teas are available to order.

Great Hound Tor `X`

Booking: 0870 770 8868
Arrival number: 01647 221202

A former farmhouse, on the eastern edge of Dartmoor near the
village of Manaton, in the shadow of Houndtor. Also close to
Haytor, Saddle Tor and Widecombe in the Moor. There are two
upstairs sleeping galleries. The ground floor has a shower, toilets
and a large recreation and cooking area. Wood is available for the
open fire. No dogs please.

Lopwell `X`

Booking: 0870 770 8868

This barn is on the banks of the river Tavy, in an Area of
Outstanding Natural Beauty on the edge of Dartmoor, on the route
of the new Tamar Valley Discovery Trail. An ideal location for
walking, cycling, canoeing and birdwatching. The sleeping area is
on the first floor. There is a shower, toilets adjacent, cooking area
with a microwave and sitting areas on the ground floor. Due to the
close proximity of neighbours, this barn is not available for hire for
parties.

Lydford `X`

Booking: 0870 770 8868
Arrival number: 01822 820206

This barn, at the Fox and Hounds Hotel, close to the village of
Lydford, has direct access onto the western edge of Dartmoor.
There are two sleeping areas, each with six bunk beds. The barn
has electric light, but no catering area, although the adjacent pub
serves breakfast and other meals. Some facilities will possibly be
shared with campers.

The South West

CAMPING BARN

Mullacott Farm   X

Booking: 0870 770 8868
Arrival number: 01271 866877

These newly renovated former stables are on a small working farm in an Area of Outstanding Natural Beauty in Exmoor. Main sleeping areas are above ground platforms and 6 bunk beds. The barn sleeps 8 in one large area, plus small 'stalls' each sleeping 2 - 4. Covered storage area and picnic area. Dogs welcome.

Northcombe   X

Booking: 0870 770 8868
Arrival number: 01398 323602

Northcombe barns are situated at Northcombe Farm one mile from Dulverton, with spectacular views and walks up to 1000 feet on the farm and footpaths and bridleways, which lead up to the moor. The River Barle is nearby for canoeing and Wimbleball Lake is only six miles away. There are two barns (A and B), one sleeping 15 and the other 22.

Runnage   X

Booking: 0870 770 8868
Arrival number: 01822 880222

Two barns - one a former table hay loft and shippon, the other converted stables - on a traditional working farm in the centre of Dartmoor, close to Bellever Forest and the River Dart. A great location for walking, cycling, climbing, letterboxing and canoeing. Mountain bikes available for hire on site. Minimum two night sole use bookings accepted at weekends and Bank Holidays.

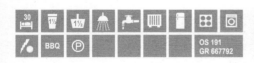

Woodadvent   X

Booking: 0870 770 8868
Arrival number: 01984 640920

In the farmyard just a mile from the village of Roadwater, this former cider barn still has the original cider press in situ. This is a quiet, unspoilt corner of Exmoor National Park, with an excellent network of footpaths. There are two separate sleeping areas, one upstairs and one downstairs, with the cooking and recreation area on the ground floor. Breakfast is available.

Home Counties and the South East Coast

Include a day trip to London during a stay at any of our properties in this region. This area offers great outdoor opportunities and many great days out. Bustling cities such as Brighton and Oxford are well known for their historic and cultural attractions. The New Forest, The Isle of Wight and The Ridgeway have long been popular with outdoor enthusiasts.

Brighton Royal Pavilion
britainonview / brightononview

For information and to book visit **www.yha.org.uk** or call **0870 770 8868**

Dover Castle

The Needles, Isle of Wight
britainonview / Martin Brent

Oxford

Family Facilities

Alfriston	43	Margate	47
Arundel	43	Medway	47
Brighstone	43	Oxford	48
Burley	44	Sandown	48
Canterbury	44	Streatley	48
Dover	45	Totland Bay	50
Ivinghoe	46	The Ridgeway	48
Jordans	46	Truleigh Hill	50
Littlehampton	46		

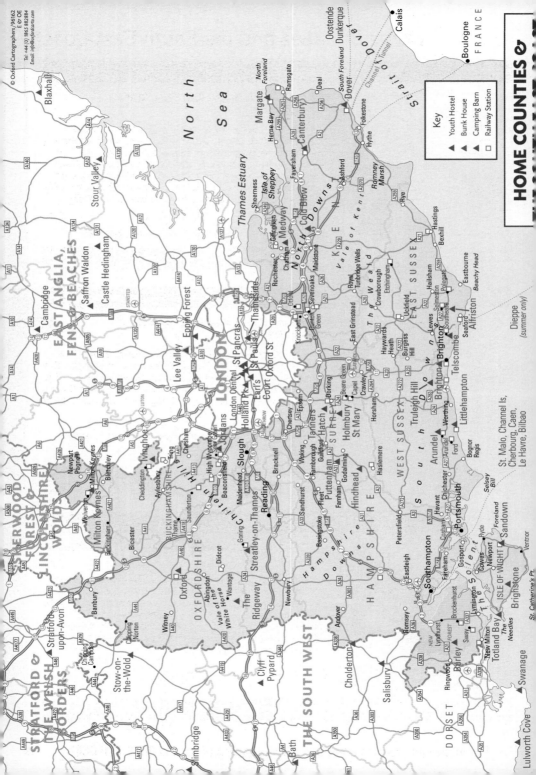

HOME COUNTIES &

Key

▲ Youth Hostel
▲ Bunk House
▲ Camping Barn
◻ Railway Station

© Oxford Cartographers / 96162
E & OE
Tel: +44 (0) 1865 882884
Email: info@oxfordcarts.com

FRANCE
Calais
Boulogne
Dunkerque
Oostende
Dieppe
(summer only)
St. Malo, Channel Is,
Cherbourg, Caen,
Le Havre, Bilbao

Strait of Dover
Channel Tunnel

North Sea

Thames Estuary
Thames Estuary

LONDON
St Pancras
London Central
St Paul's
Oxford St
Earl's Court
Holland Pk

EAST ANGLIA, FENS & BEACHES
Cambridge
Saffron Walden
Castle Hedingham
Blaxhall
Stour Valley

SHERWOOD FOREST & LINCOLNSHIRE WOLDS

STRATFORD & THE WELSH BORDERS
Stratford-upon-Avon
Chipping Campden
Stow-on-the-Wold
Bredbridge

THE SOUTH WEST
Bath
Salisbury
Cholderton
Clyff Pypard

DORSET
Swanage
Lulworth Cove

North Foreland
South Foreland
Margate
Ramsgate
Deal
Dover
Folkestone
Hythe
Herne Bay
Canterbury
Faversham
Isle of Sheppey
Sheerness
Medway
Rochester
Maidstone
Ashford
Romney Marsh
Rye
Hastings
Bexhill
Eastbourne
Beachy Head
Hailsham
Alfriston
Seaford
Newhaven
Brighton
Telscombe
Lewes
Uckfield
Crowborough
Royal Tunbridge Wells
East Grinstead
Burgess Hill
Haywards Heath

North Downs
Sevenoaks
Chaffinch
Cliftonville

Vale of Kent
The Weald
East Sussex
West Sussex
South Downs

Dorking
Horsham
Crawley
Beare Green
Capel
Tanners Hatch
Holmbury St Mary
Haslemere
Hindhead
Godalming
Guildford
Farnham
Puttenham
Woking
Farnborough
Chertsey
Epsom
Knockholt

SURREY
Truleigh Hill
Arundel
Littlehampton
Worthing
Bognor Regis
Selsey Bill
Chichester
Havant
Petersfield
Portsmouth
Gosport
Fareham
Southampton
Eastleigh
Romsey
Andover
Newbury

HAMPSHIRE
Hampshire Downs

ISLE OF WIGHT
Cowes
Newport
Ryde
Sandown
Ventnor
Brighstone
St Catherine's Pt
The Needles
Totland Bay
Lymington
Brockenhurst
Sway
Burley
New Milton
Ringwood
Lyndhurst
NEW FOREST
The Solent
Foreland

OXFORDSHIRE
Oxford
Witney
Abingdon
Wantage
Didcot
The Ridgeway
Vale of the White Horse
Chipping Norton
Banbury
Bicester
Buckingham

BUCKINGHAMSHIRE
Milton Keynes
Newport Pagnell
Wolverton
Bletchley
Aylesbury
Thame
Saunderton
Cheddington
Tring
Ivinghoe
Wendover

Chiltern Hills
High Wycombe
Beaconsfield
Marlow
Maidenhead
Slough
Bracknell
Reading
Streatley-on-Thames
Goring
Sandhurst
Heat
Basingstoke
Fleet

St Albans
Chesham
New Green
Amersham

Epping Forest
Lee Valley

WEST SUSSEX
Ford

Home Counties and the South East Coast

Alfriston F

Frog Firle, Alfriston, Polegate, East Sussex BN26 5TT
Tel: 0870 770 5666

This 16th century Sussex flint house, just outside the pretty village of Alfriston, has a Tudor beamed lounge and a large garden. The network of footpaths and bridleways, National cycle route 2 and good public transport links make YHA Alfriston ideal for exploring the South Downs and Sussex towns. Popular with families, it is 3 miles from the sea and Seven Sisters cliffs, with castles, galleries and nature reserves to explore. Pretty Alfriston village offers teashops and the National Trust Clergy House.

Accommodation: 68 beds: 7x2-4-, 7x5-8- and 1x10-bed rooms.

8.30-10.00am
5.00-11.00pm

Arundel ★★★★ B

Warningcamp, Arundel, West Sussex BN18 9QY
Tel: 0870 770 5676

This elegant Georgian mansion, set in its own grounds, is a mile from Arundel and close to the 'Blue Flag' sandy beaches at Littlehampton. Ever popular with families, the hostel has a great restaurant and bar as well as a games room and spacious garden. Children love nearby Arundel Castle, and its adjacent open air swimming pool. Hostel reception opens at 2.30pm in summer.

Accommodation: 65 beds: 2-, 3-, 4-, 5- and 6-bed rooms, 3 en-suite rooms with double beds.

8.00-10.00am
5.00-11.00pm

Brighstone X

c/o YHA Totland Bay, Hurst Hill, Totland Bay, Isle of Wight PO39 0HD
Tel: 0870 770 6070

Only open to YHA in school summer holidays, this is a modern purpose-built self-catering property owned by the Scouting Association. Tucked in the charming village of Brighstone, it is just a mile from the beach and the chalk downs. Visit the nearby Isle of Wight Pearl, for an amazing collection of pearls or take a short drive to Compton Bay for the best surfing on the Island. Here the coastline is famous for its preserved dinosaur footprints, a real hit with children.

Accommodation: 12 beds: 2x6-bed rooms.

8.00-10.00am
5.00-9.00pm

Home Counties and the South East Coast

Brighton   F

Patcham Place, London Road, Brighton, East Sussex BN1 8YD
Tel: 0870 770 5724

Nestling at the foot of the South Downs, this 16th Century manor house is three miles from Brighton city centre in open parkland. Sample fantastic shopping in Brighton's Lanes, visit the world-famous pier and impressive Royal Pavilion, museums and theatres for Brighton's lively arts scene. Countryside lovers should visit Beachy Head, Devil's Dyke or Ditchling Beacon, the highest point in Sussex. Try one of our home-cooked evening meals before venturing into this buzzing city.

Accommodation: 56 beds: 1x4-, 3x6-, 1x10- and 2x12-bed rooms.

8.00-10.00am
1.00-11.00pm

Burley   C

Cott Lane, Burley, Ringwood, Hampshire BH24 4BB
Tel: 0870 770 5734

In extensive grounds, this former family home offers easy access to the New Forest and the beaches at Lymington and Bournemouth. Hire a bike or pony for a ride in the New Forest or a canoe for a paddle on the Beaulieu River. Ferries run to the Isle of Wight from Lymington or take deep sea fishing trips from Keyhaven. The Beaulieu Motor Museum and Buckler's Hard Maritime Museum are great for rainy days. Good food is served here and at both of the local pubs.

Accommodation: 36 beds: 1x4-, 1x6-, 2x8- and 1x10-bed rooms.

8.00-10.00am
5.00-10.00pm

Canterbury   D

54 New Dover Road, Canterbury, CT1 3DT
Tel: 0870 770 5744

Canterbury is England's second most visited city after London and it is easy to see why. Its links with English monarchs and figures such as Geoffrey Chaucer and Thomas Becket have ensured enduring popularity with tourists. Stay in this Victorian gothic villa, well-placed for exploring the city or the North Downs. The energetic can hire a bike and tour the 'Crab & Winkle Way' from Canterbury to Whitstable.

Accommodation: 70 beds: 1x1-, 1x2-, 1x3-, 2x5-, 4x6- and 3x10-bed rooms.

7.30-10.00am
3.00-11.00pm

For information and to book visit **www.yha.org.uk** or call **0870 770 8868**

Home Counties and the South East Coast

Dover F

306 London Road, Dover, Kent CT17 0SY
Tel: 0870 770 5798

Just a mile from the busiest terminal port in the world, this large, Georgian building offers a friendly welcome to those heading to and from the continent. You can even get your Euros and ferry tickets here. There's plenty to do in and around Dover too. The Castle has many interactive exhibits and there are tours through the secret wartime tunnels. The White Cliffs and the South Foreland Lighthouse can be explored on foot. Breakfast is included in the price.

Accommodation: 64 beds: 3x2-, 1x4-, 1x6-, 6x8-bed rooms.

7.00-10.30am
5.00-11.00pm

Hindhead ★★ D

Devil's Punchbowl, off Portsmouth Road, Thursley, Godalming, Surrey GU8 6NS. Tel: 0870 770 5864

Set in beautiful, tranquil surroundings, this cosy retreat comprises a huddle of self-catering National Trust cottages in great walking country. Birdworld at Holt Pound in Farnham has an Underwater World while the Rural Life Centre at Tilford provides a fascinating insight into village and country life over the past 200 years. Nearby Haslemere Educational Museum invites visitors to travel through time, from pre-historic fossils to Egyptian pyramids and Victorian artefacts. To buy supplies for a meal in or visit a pub for a meal out, visit Hindhead, Graysholt or Haslemere.

Accommodation: 12 beds: 2x2-, 2x4-bed rooms.

8.00-10.00am
5.00-10.00pm

Holmbury St Mary ★ F

Radnor Lane, Dorking, Surrey RH5 6NW
Tel: 0870 770 5868

Set in wooded grounds close to this village between Dorking and Guildford and close to Holmbury Hill, which has panoramic views of the North and South Downs. You'll find 4,000 acres of woodland - great for walking, mountain biking and horse riding. The magnificent Polesden Lacey, offers tours of its elegant Edwardian interiors and is well worth a visit. Freshly cooked food is available on-site or an excellent pub nearby for nights out.

Accommodation: 46 beds: 3x2- and 10x4-bed rooms.

8.00-10.00am
5.00-10.00pm

CITY

COUNTRYSIDE

COUNTRYSIDE

For information and to book visit **www.yha.org.uk** or call **0870 770 8868**

Home Counties and the South East Coast

Ivinghoe F

High Street, Ivinghoe, Leighton Buzzard, Bedfordshire LU7 9EP
Tel: 0870 770 5884

This large Georgian house in the picturesque Buckinghamshire village is a great base for walking and cycling on the Ridgeway and in the Chilterns. Short trips out include Whipsnade Wildlife Park and Woburn Abbey and Safari Park. There are miles of lanes for cycling close by plus the Aston Hill mountain bike area. Hearty meals are served on-site or there's a pub and a restaurant nearby.

Accommodation: 50 beds: 2x5-, 2x6-, 1x8- and 2x10-bed rooms.

      7.30-10.00am 5.00-10.30pm

Jordans C

Welders Lane, Jordans, Beaconsfield, Buckinghamshire HP9 2SN
Tel: 0870 770 5886

In a village with a long Quaker heritage, this is a tranquil place to stay near the famous Mayflower Barn and 17th Century Friends' Meeting House. John Milton's Cottage in Chalfont St Giles is where this blind genius sought to avoid the plague. Bekonscot Model Village, set in an idyllic 1930s time warp and linked by one of the UK's biggest model railways. Jordans is self-catering only but with a good choice of local eateries. Light breakfast available on request. Private rooms available. Only 12 miles from Windsor and 15 miles from Heathrow airport.

Accommodation: 22 beds: 2x5- and 2x6-bed rooms.

          9.00-10.00am 5.00-10.30pm

Littlehampton ★★★★ B

Littlehampton, West Sussex, BN17 5AW
Tel: 0870 770 6114

Cosy and fun with a distinctive nautical feel, this modern facility is part of the newly developed Fisherman's Wharf complex, right on the harbour-side. A few yards away is the gently-shelving Blue Flag beach, a massive expanse of fine sand at low tide. With many small ensuite rooms, families love it here and it's ideal for a bucket and spade break. Local attractions include Arundel Castle or the Military Aviation Museum. There's also a good café within the complex.

Accommodation: 32 beds: 3-, 4- and 5-bedded rooms

          8.00-10.00am 5.00-9.00pm

For information and to book visit **www.yha.org.uk** or call **0870 770 8868**

Margate A

3-4 Royal Esplanade, Westbrook Bay, Margate, Kent CT9 5DL
Tel: 0870 770 5956

A former hotel overlooking Westbrook Bay's 'blue flag' beach and an ideal place for a fun-packed family holiday. Margate has been popular with Londoners for more than 200 years and has amusement arcades and souvenir shops aplenty. But it also has hidden delights, like the Shell Grotto, Margate Caverns and Dreamland Theme Park. Broadstairs and Ramsgate offer a rather more genteel seaside experience. It's self-catering only here but there are plenty of places to eat in town.

Accommodation: 60 beds: 2x6-, 2x5-, 6x4-, 2x3-, and 4x2-bed rooms.

8.00-10.00am
5.00-11.00pm

Medway F

Capstone Road, Gillingham, Kent ME7 3JE
Tel: 0870 770 5964

This former traditional Kentish oasthouse offers a high standard of accommodation and an ideal base from which to explore its history-rich surroundings. Chatham's Royal Dockyard Museum celebrates our maritime heritage and is home to three historic warships. Charles Dickens lived at Eastgate House in Rochester and died at nearby Gad's Hill. Leeds Castle, near Maidstone, is also worth a visit.

Accommodation: 40 beds: 4x2-, 1x3-, 6x4- and 1x5-bed rooms.

8.00-10.00am
5.00-10.00pm

Milton Keynes F

Vicarage Road, Milton Keynes, Buckinghamshire, MK13 9AG
Tel: 0870 770 5716

An attractive, converted 18th Century farmhouse, conveniently located to explore Buckinghamshire`s many attractions. Close by is Xscape, offering year round, indoor winter sports, 16 cinema screens and a 43ft tall climbing wall. Bletchley Park, home of the Second World War code-breakers, is also a very short drive away as are Woburn Abbey Safari Park, Silverstone and Gulliver's Land. Breakfast available. There is great food served on the premises.

Accommodation: 37 beds: 1x1-, 3x4-, 1x5-, 1x9- and 1x10-bed rooms.

8.00-10.00am
5.00-10.00pm

Home Counties and the South East Coast

CITY

Oxford ★★★★ A

2a Botley Road, Oxford, Oxfordshire OX2 0AB
Tel: 0870 770 5970

Next door to the railway station, this modern, purpose-built accommodation offers first class facilities. Hire a bike from reception and enjoy cycling around this beautiful, historic city. A tour of the Ashmolean Museum, the oldest museum in the UK, is a must as is a visit to the high-tech Oxford Story Museum with an indoor ride through 900 years of university history. Enjoy great food in our restaurant or at one of the many others to be found nearby.

Accommodation: 184 beds: 8x2-, 12x4- and 20x6-bed rooms.

   24 hours

COAST

Sandown ★★★ E

The Firs, Fitzroy Street, Sandown, Isle of Wight PO36 8JH
Tel: 0870 770 6020

The buckets and spades available on free loan from reception are a good indicator of the kind of guests that enjoy staying here. For sun, fun, sea and sand, the busy town of Sandown is a popular holiday resort on the east coast of the Isle of Wight. The zoo, Dinosaur Isle, Tiger Sanctuary, Robin Hill and Blackgang Chine are just a few of the attractions close by. Enjoy a home cooked meal with us in the evening or venture out to one of the many restaurants and pubs.

Accommodation: 47 beds: 3x2-, 6x4-, 1x5- and 2x6-bed rooms.

  E2 L4R      8.00-11.00am
5.00-10.00pm

COUNTRYSIDE

Streatley-on-Thames ★★★ B

Reading Road, Streatley, Berkshire RG8 9JJ
Tel: 0870 770 6054

A comfortable Victorian house on one of the prettiest stretches of the Thames is great for strolling along the river banks or walking The Ridgeway. Fun and creativity combine at nearby Legoland Windsor to provide a memorable family excursion while Beale Adventure Park has exotic plants and animals in abundance. The Living Rainforest at Wyld Court is the only example of its kind in the UK. In the evenings, dine with us or visit pubs in Streatley, or Goring, over the river.

Accommodation: 48 beds: 1x2-, 3x4-, 2x5- and 4x6-bed rooms.

  E2 L4R   8.00-10.00am
5.00-10.30pm

For information and to book visit **www.yha.org.uk** or call **0870 770 8868**

Home Counties and the South East Coast

Tanners Hatch

  E

off Ranmore Road, Dorking, Surrey RH5 6BE
Tel: 0870 770 6060

This self-catering cottage in National Trust woodlands has masses of character, including log fires and herb garden! Only accessible on foot, it sits on footpaths around the Surrey Hills Area of Outstanding Natural Beauty. Nearby is Polesden Lacey, a regency mansion with stunning Edwardian Gardens, while children love to feed the animals at Bockett`s Working Farm at Fetcham. Chessington World of Adventure is also nearby. Packed breakfasts available.

Accommodation: 25 beds: 1x7- and 2x9-bed rooms.

L4R   BBQ

8.00-10.00am
5.00-10.00pm

Telscombe

★ E

Bank Cottages, Telscombe, Lewes, East Sussex BN7 3HZ
Tel: 0870 770 6062

A row of 18th Century self-catering cottages in this tiny, attractive village provides an ideal base to explore the South Downs. The area is indelibly linked with The Bloomsbury Group, a literary circle that strongly influenced the British cultural scene during the first half of the 20th Century. Monk's House was the country home of Leonard and Virginia Woolf and six miles away is Charleston Farmhouse, former residence of artists Duncan Grant and Vanessa Bell, who decorated it in their own distinctive style. Buy fresh fish and meat from the local farm.

Accommodation: 22 beds: 1x2- and 5x4-bed rooms.

E2

8.00-10.00am
5.00-10.00pm

The Ridgeway

★ ★ ★ D

Court Hill, Wantage, Oxfordshire OX12 9NE
Tel: 0870 770 6064

The Ridgeway National Trail runs for 87 miles through the ancient landscapes and secluded wooded valleys of Oxfordshire; a route used since prehistoric times by travellers and herdsmen. Close to it is YHA The Ridgeway, a beautifully kept cluster of converted barns, arranged around a courtyard in extensive grounds. Six miles from here you'll find Uffington's famous White Horse and 3,000-year-old castle. Enjoy a meal in or have a BBQ in the grounds!

Accommodation: 59 beds: 1x2-, 6x4-, 1x5-, 1x6-, 1x9- and 1x13-bed rooms.

             BBQ

7.15-10.00am
5.00-11.00pm

COUNTRYSIDE
COUNTRYSIDE
COUNTRYSIDE

Home Counties and the South East Coast

Totland Bay ★★★ E

Hurst Hill, Totland Bay, Isle of Wight PO39 0HD
Tel: 0870 770 6070

On the Isle of Wight's west coast, Totland Bay is a delightful sandy beach with waterfront restaurant and pier. Our accommodation is a stone's throw from it in a large, private Victorian house. Colwell Bay is an easy walk along the promenade but nothing's too far away on this compact island. The Needles Pleasure Park and Alum Bay with its stomach-churning lift are within easy reach. In the evenings, enjoy a meal in our restaurant or venture out to nearby pubs and cafes.

Accommodation: 60 beds: 3x2-, 7x4- (1 ensuite), 3x6- and 1x8-bed rooms.

8.00-10.00am
5.00-10.00pm

Truleigh Hill ★★★ B

Tottington Barn, Shoreham-by-Sea, West Sussex BN43 5FB
Tel: 0870 770 6078

In the South Downs National Park, just inland from coastal towns of Shoreham and Worthing, you'll find this modern, purpose-built accommodation with a pleasant open garden away from busy roads. It caters particularly well for families and our home cooked menus are a hit with kids. The magnificent views across the hills towards Devil's Dyke are a permanent temptation for walkers and cyclists while the less energetic can visit stylish Brighton or the more sedate Hove.

Accommodation: 56 beds: some 2-4-, mostly 6-bed rooms.

7.30-10.00am
5.00-10.30pm

Puttenham X

Booking: 0870 770 6060
Arrival number: 01483 811001

Set amidst beautiful countryside on the North Downs Way National Trail, five miles from Guildford and the River Wey, this sustainable camping barn in the village of Puttenham boasts solar panels and a rainwater harvesting scheme. The barn is excellent for walkers and cyclists, with Sustrans cycle route 22 passing the door. There is no motor access - even for off-loading. With attractions like the Watts Gallery in Compton less than two miles away, Puttenham village is an ideal base for exploring the Surrey Hills.

OS 145
GR 933479

Cold Blow X

Booking: 0870 770 8868
Arrival time: 01622 735038

A camping barn and two bunk barns near Maidstone in Kent. On the boundary of the farm is the North Downs Way National Trail and close by is the Pilgrim's Way. YHA Kemsing is nearby, making it convenient for a stop on a short walking tour. Enjoy visits to Chatham Dockyard and Leeds Castle. The 'Old Bunk Barn' sleeps 10 in 3 rooms with kitchen/dining area. The 'New Bunk Barn' sleeps up to 41 in 7 rooms and has an open plan double kitchen and large dining/meeting room. Dogs must be under strict control. Stabling/grazing for horses can be booked direct with the owner.

OS 188
GR 822580

For information and to book visit **www.yha.org.uk** or call **0870 770 8868**

Escape to...

Mansions, Lodges and Cottages for exclusive hire

YHA Exeter

51

East Anglia, Fens and Beaches

Be sure to pack a bucket and spade or a pair of binoculars for a trip to the beautiful Norfolk coast with its lovely beaches and abundant bird life.

Beautiful cities like Cambridge and Norwich offer plenty of cultural and historic interest and the sleepy Suffolk Sandlings is an ideal venue to get away from it all.

Sheringham Promenade
britainonview / John Whit

For information and to book visit **www.yha.org.uk** or call **0870 770 8868**

Seals at Blakeney Point

Kings College Chapel, Cambridge
www.britainonview.com

Family Facilities

Blaxhall	55
Castle Hedingham	55
Epping Forest	56
Great Yarmouth	56
Hunstanton	56
Lee Valley	57
Sheringham	58
Wells-next-the-Sea	58

For information and to book visit **www.yha.org.uk** or call **0870 770 8868**

EAST ANGLIA, FENS & BEACHES

Key

- ▲ Youth Hostel
- ▲ Bunk House
- ▲ Camping Barn
- ▲ Guest House
- ▢ Railway Station

North Sea

SHERWOOD FOREST & LINCOLNSHIRE WOLDS

Redhurst
Woody's Top
Lincoln
Thurlby

The Wash
Hunstanton
Burnham Market
Blakeney Pt.
Wells-next-the-Sea
Sheringham
Cromer

King's Lynn
Fakenham
Wisbech
Swaffham
East Dereham
Norfolk Broads
NORWICH
Norwich
Great Yarmo[uth]

Peterborough
March
Downham Market
Mundford
Wymondham
Lowes[toft]
Beccles

CAMBRIDGESHIRE
Chatteris
Ely
Mildenhall
Thetford
Diss
Saxmundham

Huntingdon
St. Ives
Girton
Newmarket
Bury St. Edmunds
SUFFOLK
Blaxhall
Aldeburgh

St. Neots
Cambridge
Stowmarket
Wickham Market
Claydon
Woodbridge
Orford Ness

BEDFORDSHIRE
Bedford
Biggleswade
Royston
Great Chesterford
Haverhill
Sudbury
Stour Valley
Ipswich
Felixstowe

Kempston
Milton Keynes
Saffron Walden
Audley End
Castle Hedingham
Harwich
The Naze

Letchworth
HERTFORD-SHIRE
Stansted
Braintree
Marks Tey
Colchester
Walton on the Naze

Leighton Buzzard
Hitchin
Stevenage
STANSTED
Witham
Clacton-on-Sea

Dunstable
Luton
Harpenden
Welwyn Garden City
Bishop's Stortford
ESSEX
Mersea I.
Colne Pt.

Ivinghoe
Tring
Berkhamsted
St. Albans
Hertford
Harlow
Hoddesdon
Chelmsford
Maldon

Jordans
Watford
Hatfield
Potters Bar
Cheshunt
Billericay
Crouch
Foulness Pt.
Foulness I.

Epping Forest
Brentwood
Basildon
Rayleigh
SOUTHEND
Southend-on-Sea
Shoebury Ness

LONDON
St Pancras
LONDON
Oxford St
Holland Park
Earl's Ct
St Pauls
Thameside
Grays
Tilbury
Canvey
Thames Estuary

London Central

Margate

Medway
Canterbury

Tanners Hatch
Holmbury St Mary
Hindhead
Cold Blow
Dover

HOME COUNTIES & THE SOUTH EAST COAST

Strait of Dover
Channel Tunnel

Esbjerg, Ham[burg]
Hoek van Ho[lland]

Oost Dunke[rk]
Boulogne

© Oxford Cartographers/96162
E & OE
Tel: +44 (0) 1865 882884
Email: info@oxfordcarta.com

East Anglia, Fens and Beaches

Blaxhall

Heath Walk, Blaxhall, Woodbridge, Suffolk IP12 2EA
Tel: 0870 770 5702

This former school in Blaxhall is on the edge of the Suffolk Sandlings, 20 miles north of Ipswich. Winner of a Green Tourism Award, it makes a perfect base for bird-watching, cycling and walking in this Area of Outstanding Natural Beauty. Nearby Sutton Hoo, at Woodbridge, is home to a complete 7th Century burial ship of an Anglo-Saxon king, laden with artefacts, while Orford is famous for its shellfish, particularly fresh oysters. Good food, using the excellent local produce, is served on-site.

Accommodation: 40 beds: 1x2-, 2x4- and 5x6-bed rooms.

7.30-10.00am
5.00-10.30pm

Cambridge ★★★ A

97 Tenison Road, Cambridge, Cambridgeshire CB1 2DN
Tel: 0870 770 5742

Cambridge is one of the most cosmopolitan and culturally diverse cities in England and you will meet visitors from all over the world in this former Victorian townhouse. Take a punt on the River Cam, or hire a bicycle and navigate the many cycle friendly routes around this university town. Don't miss the Fitzwilliam Museum, home of the university's vast art collection or the Imperial War Museum at nearby Duxford. Good food and a bar available here, or there are plenty of different night-life options in town.

Accommodation: 99 beds: 2-, 3-, 4-, 6- and 8-bed rooms.

7.00am -
10.30 pm

Castle Hedingham ★ F

7 Falcon Square, Castle Hedingham, Essex CO9 3BU
Tel: 0870 770 5756

This 16th Century building with its own large, lawned garden in Essex is an ideal place to sample traditional English village life. Visit the castle itself, an imposing structure originally built shortly after the Norman conquest of 1066 or the Colne Valley Heritage Railway based at the former village station. The Roman city of Colchester and Constable Country are also within easy reach for excursions. Good, home-cooked meals are also a speciality of the house.

Accommodation: 50 beds: 1x2-, 1x4-, 1x8-, 2x6- and 2x10+-bed rooms.

7.30-10.00am
5.00-10.30pm

East Anglia, Fens and Beaches

Epping Forest   C

Wellington Hill, High Beach, Loughton, Essex IG10 4AG
Tel: 0870 770 5822

In a former pavilion, in 6,000 acres of former royal hunting forest, just 10 miles from London, you'll find YHA Epping Forest. Attractions close by include: Paradise Wildlife Park near Hoddesdon with three, themed adventure playgrounds or the biggest, deepest, Cold War Secret Nuclear Bunker at Kelvedon Hatch. The Royal Gunpowder Mills at Waltham Abbey are also worth a look. It's self-catering only but there are three decent local pubs if you can't face cooking.

Accommodation: 32 beds: 6x4-, 1x6- and 1x2 bed rooms

           8.00-10.00am
5.00-11.00pm

Great Yarmouth   F

2 Sandown Road, Great Yarmouth, Norfolk NR30 1EY
Tel: 0870 770 5840

Great Yarmouth seafront recently had a £16 million 'face-lift' to give it a more continental feel. This former Edwardian family hotel is just minutes away, so pack your bucket and spade and prepare to enjoy a traditional seaside holiday. Enjoy hours of white knuckle fun with over 70 rides and attractions at Pleasure Beach Amusement Park or visit Pettit's Animal Adventure Park, Redwings Horse Sanctuary and Thrigby Hall Wildlife Gardens for calmer alternatives. It's great for exploring the Norfolk Broads too.

Accommodation: 40 beds: 1x2-, 2x4-, 2x6-, 1x8- and 1x10-bed rooms.

            8.00-10.00am
5.00-10.00pm

Hunstanton ★★★ D

15 Avenue Road, Hunstanton, Norfolk PE36 5BW
Tel: 0870 770 5872

Nicknamed 'Sunny Hunny' by locals, Hunstanton gets its fair share of blue skies and uniquely for a town on the Norfolk Coast, it faces west, so the sunsets here are a real treat. We provide good food and accommodation in two Victorian townhouses minutes from the centre and within easy reach of gently-shelving, sandy beaches - great for little legs! The Norfolk Coast Path and Peddars Way are close by and are great for wildlife spotting, or you can take a boat trip to the nearby Seal Island.

Accommodation: 41 beds: 2x2-, 1x3-, 5x4-, 1x6 and 1x8-bed rooms.

               8.00-10.00am
5.00-10.00pm

For information and to book visit **www.yha.org.uk** or call **0870 770 8868**

East Anglia, Fens and Beaches

King's Lynn   F

Thoresby College, College Lane, King's Lynn, Norfolk PE30 1JB
Tel: 0870 770 5902

This 500-year-old Chantry College building is in the historic part of King's Lynn - known locally as the capital of West Norfolk. Many historic and pretty buildings line its cobbled streets and the surrounding countryside is great for bird-watching, walking or cycling. Other attractions include the Queen's country residence at Sandringham, Houghton Hall, built in the 18th Century by Sir Robert Walpole and the Norman ruins of Castle Rising and Castle Acre. Breakfast available. Evening meals are only available for pre-booked groups.

Accommodation: 35 beds: 1x1-, 1x3-, 2x6-, 1x9- and 1x10-bed rooms.

   8.00-10.00am 5.00-11.00 pm

Lee Valley  A

Windmill Lane, Cheshunt, Hertfordshire, EN8 9AJ
Tel: 0870 770 6118

Relaxing in this peaceful haven set in 10,000 acres of Country Park and waterways, it is hard to believe that London's Liverpool Street Station is just a 20-minute train ride away. Our six waterside log cabins next door to an activity centre offer a perfect urban escape as well as a chance to try sailing, kayaking, caving, climbing and canoeing (advance booking essential). Excellent cycling, walking, bird watching and orienteering not to mention fine food is also found here and kids love the Hayes Hill petting farm nearby.

Accommodation: 114 beds: 2-, 3-, 4-, 6- and 8-bed rooms

                 24hrs

Saffron Walden   F

1 Myddylton Place, Saffron Walden, Essex CB10 1BB
Tel: 0870 770 6014

For a real taste of medieval living, a stay at this 600-year-old former maltings is a must. Saffron Walden is one of England's best-preserved historic market towns and we are based in its oldest inhabited building, complete with oak beams, uneven floors and a walled garden. The Imperial War Museum is close by at Duxford, there's a Jacobean mansion at Audley End House and children love the otters and flamingos at Mole Hall Wildlife Park at Widdington. Good food is served here too.

Accommodation: 40 beds: 4x2-6- and 2x10-12-bed rooms

      7.30-10.00am 5.00-11.00pm

East Anglia, Fens and Beaches

Sheringham   ★★ D

1 Cremer's Drift, Sheringham, Norfolk NR26 8HX
Tel: 0870 770 6024

Head for the Norfolk coast and discover all that's great about the traditional British seaside holiday. There are plenty of small, private family rooms and some of the country's best beaches lie just a short walk away. Great facilities are provided on-site but if you choose to venture out, there's a steam railway and Shire Horse Centre close by or you can see the seals on boat trips from Blakeney. Breakfast included in the price. Dinner is available here and food fans should note the town has a thriving shell-fishing industry.

Accommodation: 100 beds:10x2-, 6x3-, 8x4- and 5x6- bed rooms.

       9.00-10.30am / 1.00-11.00pm

Wells-next-the-Sea   ★★★★ A

Church Plain, Wells, Norfolk NR23 1EQ
Tel: 0870 770 6084

Whether bird watching, buckets and spades or bumbling about on coastal paths are your thing, our self-catering property in this bustling fishing village is ideal. Wells is the mid-point on the North Norfolk Coast Path, where the quays teem with yachts and fishing boats. Discover creeks and salt marshes brimming with birdlife, miles of empty beaches or take a boat trip to see a seal colony. In the evening, go 'crabbing' on the quayside, cook the day's catch or try some of the best fish and chips in the land.

Accommodation: 31 beds: 2x2-3-bed, 1x2, 1x3- and 5x4-bed rooms.

        8.00-10.00am / 5.00-10.00pm

Stour Valley F 3

Brantham Hall, Manningtree, Essex CO11 1PT
Tel: 01473 327090 Bookings: 0870 770 8868

This newly opened bunkhouse offers comfortable accommodation on a historic Suffolk farm close to the Stour Estuary and Constable Country. The coastal path runs along the shore and Seafield Bay only five minutes walk is a haven for birdwatchers. Nearby Alton Water provides dinghy and board sailing, walks and cycles for hire. The bunkhouse is set in a peaceful location with pub and store nearby but the nightlife of Ipswich Waterfront is only six miles away.

 Access by arrangement

YHA Buffet Breakfasts

Enjoy a relaxing buffet breakfast with a selection of pastries, hot favourites and chilled items to tempt you.

If you fancy a traditional cooked breakfast with all the trimmings, ask staff on booking for details. Ingredients for this British classic cost a little more than our standard breakfast, therefore a modest supplement may apply.

For more information on breakfasts at your chosen YHA visit the website at www.yha.org.uk

Sherwood Forest and Lincolnshire Wolds

Sherwood Heath, Nottinghamshire
britainonview / Derek Forss

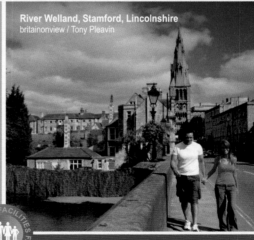

River Welland, Stamford, Lincolnshire
britainonview / Tony Pleavin

Sherwood Forest, 20 miles long by 6 miles wide is home to more than 1,000 ancient oaks and several ancient heaths - a real delight for all the family.

The fertile chalk hills that make up the Lincolnshire Wolds have been farmed for more than 4,000 years and this Area of Outstanding Natural Beauty, the highest point in eastern England, is great for outdoor activity.

Family Facilities

62   National Forest
62   Sherwood Forest
62   Thurlby

For information and to book visit **www.yha.org.uk** or call **0870 770 8868**

Sherwood Forest and Lincolnshire Wolds

National Forest

Bath Lane, Moira, Swadlincote, Derbyshire DE12 6BD
Details to be confirmed - visit the website for more information.

Due to open for summer 2007, this state-of-the-art eco and family-friendly centre gives access to the National Forest's many attractions. Top of the list has to be the award-winning Conkers complex next door - a haven for active youngsters with its discovery zones, tree-top walks, nature trails, assault courses and indoor play area. Trains on a narrow gauge railway provide a fun way of getting around and there's even a bistro/café on-site to relax in at the end of a busy day.

Accommodation: 74 beds: 2-4 bed rooms some with double beds and en-suite.

Sherwood Forest

Forest Corner, Edwinstowe, Nottinghamshire NG21 9RN
Tel: 0870 770 6026

This modern lodge is in a quiet woodland setting on the edge of Sherwood Forest. It's a short stroll to the nearby Visitor Centre and the Major Oak, reputedly the hideaway of Robin Hood. Sherwood is an ideal base to explore many stately homes such as Hardwick Hall and Newstead Abbey. Alternatively, take a bike ride to Rufford or Clumber Park, where there are many well-marked cycle paths. There's great food on offer in the restaurant and some rooms have their own private terrace.

Accommodation: 39 beds: all 2-5-bed rooms, mostly en-suite.

7.30am - 11.00pm

Thurlby ★★★ C

16 High St, Thurlby, Bourne, Lincolnshire PE10 0EE
Tel: 0870 770 6066

This 15th Century village forge enjoys a quiet village location near to the attractive market towns of Bourne, Stamford, and Market Deeping. The Fens make natural cycling country and Belton House, Belvoir Castle and Burghley House are all nearby. Rutland Water offers a great choice of watersports and walks and is an important area for bird life. Thurlby is self-catering only, but there is a pub round the corner. Serious food lovers should visit nearby Hambleton where there are two Michelin-listed restaurants.

Accommodation: 24 beds: 1x3-, 2x4-,1x5-, and 1x8- bed rooms.

BBQ

8.00-12.00am 5.00-10.00pm

Sherwood Forest and Lincolnshire Wolds

Woody's Top ★★★ E

Ruckland, Louth, Lincolnshire LN11 8RQ
Tel: 0870 770 6098

Tucked away in the Lincolnshire Wolds, this converted farm building is within easy reach of the charming market towns of Horncastle and Louth. Lincoln, with its imposing gothic cathedral is only 25 miles away. Take a drive to Skegness or escape to the RSPB reserves. The airfields of Lincolnshire are well-documented at the Aviation Heritage Centre at East Kirkby, where you can take a taxi ride in a Lancaster Bomber. Woody's Top is self-catering but there are good local pubs nearby.

Accommodation: 20 beds: 1x2-, 3x4- and 1x6-bed rooms.

    8.00-10.00am 5.00-10.00pm

It's easy to book

To check availability and make a booking visit www.yha.org.uk or phone the contact centre on 0870 770 8868

Redhurst B&B ★★★ A

Redhurst, Holton cum Beckering, Market Rasen, Lincolnshire LN8 5NG
Tel: 01673 857927

In the small Lincolnshire village of Holton Cum Beckering you'll find this attractive B&B offering a hearty breakfast. On the edge of the picturesque Lincolnshire Wolds, the Viking Way and the Hull to Harwich Cycle Route are both close by. Nearby Market Rasen is best-known for its picturesque racecourse and makes for a great day out. Lincoln is another regular day trip destination from here and the East Coast is only 30 miles away. At the end the day, sit back and relax in the garden.

Accommodation 5 beds: 1x1- and 2x2 bed rooms.

      BBQ 8.00-10.00am 4.30-10.00pm

Stratford and the Welsh Borders

Stratford-upon-Avon, the birthplace of William Shakespeare is a bustling historic town on the banks of the river Avon. A short distance to the west is Ironbridge, cradle of the Industrial Revolution.

The countryside that surrounds the England/Wales border has been described as one of the last rural idylls in Britain and is as popular with walkers as it is with wildlife enthusiasts.

Wye Valley and Forest of Dean
britainonview / Adrian Houston

For information and to book visit **www.yha.org.uk** or call **0870 770 8868**

The Ironbridge, Shropshire
www.britainonview.com

alongside canal in Birmingham
britainonview / Pawel Libera

Shakespeare's birthplace, Stratford
britainonview / Martin Brent

Family Facilities

Clun Mill	67	Stratford	69
Coalport	68	Welsh Bicknor	69
Kington	68	Wilderhope	69
Leominster	68		

For information and to book visit **www.yha.org.uk** or call **0870 770 8868**

Bridges Long Mynd

Ratlinghope, Shrewsbury, Shropshire SY5 0SP
Tel: 01588 650656

South Shropshire has been described as one of the last remaining rural idylls and after a stay in this old village school, you will see why. Those choosing to walk on the nearby Shropshire Way will see wild ponies, woodpeckers, skylarks and plenty of birds of prey. On wet days visit the charming market towns of Ludlow, Much Wenlock or Bishop's Castle. There's also the Acton Scott working farm and museum close by. In the evenings, sample our home-cooked menus or visit the pub next door.

Accommodation: 37 beds: 1x5-, 1x8-, 1x10- and 1x14-bed rooms.

     | 8.00-10.00am 5.00-10.00pm

Clun Mill   C

The Mill, Clun, Craven Arms, Shropshire SY7 8NY
Tel: 0870 770 5766.

The village of Clun, five miles south of Bishop's Castle in southern Shropshire is in the Clun Forest, an area of wild rolling hills which makes it superb walking and cycling country. This beautifully restored water mill makes a great base for exploring the unspoilt landscape and picturesque market towns nearby. The mill is a self-catering property but in the village there are two pubs that serve food nearby and the town of Ludlow - a food-lover's paradise - is a short drive away.

Accommodation: 24 beds: 1x7-bed room and 1x4-, 1x8- and 1x5-bed rooms (en-suite).

       | 8.00-10.00am 5.00-11.00pm

Coalbrookdale E

c/o High Street, Coalport, Telford, Shropshire TF8 7HT
Tel: 0870 770 5882

The Ironbridge Gorge played a major part in England's industrial history and is now a World Heritage Site and home to 10 museums. We occupy a former literary and scientific institute built in the 19th Century and within easy walking distance of Abraham Darby's famous bridge. On the banks of the Severn, it's a great spot for canoeing and fishing - with a licence - or head out to explore the beautiful Shropshire countryside. Good food is available here or at a number of places in the town.

Accommodation: 74 beds: 2x1-, 5x2-, 7x4-, 3x6- and 2x8- bed rooms.

       | 7.00-12.00am 5.00-10.30pm

Stratford and the Welsh Borders

Coalport

    **E**

John Rose Building, High Street, Coalport, Shropshire TF8 7HT
Tel: 0870 770 5882

This is an old china factory within the Ironbridge Gorge World Heritage Site, offering easy access to its many attractions and museums. National collections of Caughley and Coalport china are displayed at the china factory museum next door and it's a short walk along the Shropshire Canal to the 200-year old Tar Tunnel. Children get a fascinating insight into Victorian life at the nearby Blists Hill village or can visit Enginuity! - an interactive science museum. Good food is served here daily.

Accommodation: 85 beds: 1x1-, 4x2-, 2x3-, 8x4-, 1x5-, 1x6-, 2x8- and 1x11-bed rooms, some en-suite.

                7.00am - 10.30pm

Kington

★★★★ **C**

Victoria Road, Kington, Herefordshire HR5 3BX
Tel: 0870 770 6128

Kington is a quaint market town surrounded by stunning countryside close to Offa's Dyke on the River Arrow. The renovated Victorian Cottage Hospital provides excellent self-catering accommodation for walkers, cyclists and families. It's a great base for exploring the 40-mile circular Black and White trail. Kington is also home to Hergest Croft Gardens with its many trees and shrubs, a Small Breeds Farm with a fine collection of owls and the Judges Lodging House in Presteigne.

Accommodation: 31 beds: 1x2-, 1x3-, 4x4- and 2x5-bed rooms. Most rooms are en-suite.

              8.00- 10.00am 5.00-10.00pm

Leominster

★★★★    **B**

The Old Priory, Leominster, Herefordshire HR6 8EQ
Tel: 0870 770 5916

Our self-catering accommodation in Leominster may be modern, but the complex in which it is built is part of a 12th Century Benedictine monastery. From here, explore the narrow streets and admire medieval, Tudor and Georgian architecture. The beautiful surrounding border countryside is quiet and unspoilt and the Lindlow and Kington Mortimer trails pass close by. Visit Croft Castle with its superb collection of paintings and Berrington Hall with gardens designed by Capability Brown.

Accommodation: 30 beds: 4x2-, 2x3- and 4x4-bed rooms

             8.00-10.00am 5.00-10.00pm

Stratford-upon-Avon

  B

Hemmingford House, Alveston, Stratford-upon-Avon, Warwickshire, CV37 7RG. Tel: 0870 770 6052

This splendidly refurbished Georgian mansion in three acres of grounds is in the tranquil village of Alveston and 2 miles from Shakespeare's Birthplace. See performances by the world-renowned Royal Shakespeare Company at one of the town's theatres or take advantage of fine shopping facilities and a host of quality restaurants and cafes. Alternatively, Warwick Castle, the finest medieval castle in England is just 8 miles away. You can eat well here or at the village pub.

Accommodation: 132 beds: 1x12-, 11x2-, 8x6-, 7x4-, 2x3- and 2x8-bed rooms, some en-suite.

             7.00-12.00am

Welsh Bicknor

 E

**Near Goodrich, Ross-on-Wye, Herefordshire HR9 6JJ
Tel: 0870 770 6086**

This Victorian rectory sits in 25 acres of riverside grounds in Welsh Bicknor on the Welsh border in Herefordshire. It provides fine views of the Royal Forest of Dean as well as excellent walking and cycling from the front door. Available here are: good food, access to the River Wye and native American tipis in the grounds. Nearby see Goodrich Castle, a Hedge Puzzle and Leisure Park at Symonds Yat or the National Bird of Prey Centre at Newent. Canoe hire is available nearby.

Accommodation: 78 beds: 2x2-, 6x4-, 4x6-, 2x8- and 1x10-bed rooms.

                **8.00-10.00am
5.00-10.30pm**

Wilderhope Manor

★ ★ **F**

**Longville-in-the-Dale, Shropshire TF13 6EG
Tel: 0870 770 6090**

You can be forgiven for thinking you've taken a wrong turn as you sweep up the long drive to this National Trust-owned Elizabethan manor house. But once you've seen the oak spiral staircases, timber-framed walls and sampled our hearty home-cooking in the grand dining hall, you won't want to leave. The impressive building sits on Wenlock Edge not far from the historic Ironbridge Gorge in the heart of the Welsh Marches and offers plenty of good walking in the nearby Shropshire Hills.

Accommodation: 74 beds: 1x2-, 1x4-, 2x5-, 1x6- 2x12- and 2x14-bed rooms, some en-suite.

              **7.30-11.00am
3.00-10.30pm**

CITY

COUNTRYSIDE

COUNTRYSIDE

Stratford and the Welsh Borders

All Stretton   C

Meadow Green, Batch Valley, All Stretton, Shropshire SY6 6JW. Tel: 01694 722593

Set in the heart of the Batch Valley, this well equipped bunkhouse offers immediate access to the Long Mynd for walks, bike rides and birdwatching. For those keen on walking between hostels, All Stretton bunkhouse is a comfortable walk to YHA Bridges and YHA Clun. Church Stretton is easily accessible for a pleasant days shopping. The nearby Yew Tree Pub provides lunchtime and evening meals. Pre-book to avoid disappointment.

    Access by arrangement

Magnolia Bishops Castle   A

3 Montgomery Road, Bishop's Castle, Shropshire, SY9 5EZ Tel: 01588 638098

YHA is delighted to offer accommodation in this award-winning B&B, set in beautiful landscaped gardens and two minute's walk from the centre of Bishop's Castle. It is geared up for walkers and cyclists with a drying area, cycle storage and pick-up/drop off service to the local trails. The Shropshire Way passes close to the back gate and it is well placed for visiting Montgomery Castle as well as the National Trust's Carding Mill Valley and Long Mynd.

Accommodation: 6: 3 double, 3 twin.

Oxford Cottage   A

Oxford Cottage, Oxford Road, Hay-on-Wye, Herefordshire, HR3 5AJ Tel:01497 820008

Hay-On-Wye is a small Welsh town bang on the border with England. It's probably best known for its literary festival each spring, when it transforms into a vibrant cultural centre. This attractive Georgian townhouse offers B&B accommodation and makes an ideal base to explore the second-hand bookshops and beautiful surrounding countryside. Explore Offa's Dyke nearby, which has tremendous views of the Black Mountains and Glascwm.

Accommodation: 6 beds.

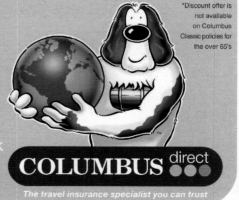

Volunteering with YHA

If you've got some free time and would like to support YHA, there are lots of volunteering projects throughout the YHA network.

You could run a hostel as a voluntary warden or help with reception, general maintenance, gardening, conservation work, organising events, fundraising, lobbying on behalf of YHA or offering administrative support.

For more information on volunteering tel: 01629 592562 or visit the website at www.yha.org.uk

Derbyshire Dales, Peaks & Staffordshire Moorlands

Some say the best parts of Derbyshire are in Staffordshire; the truth is that both counties are abound with wild craggy peaks, rolling green hills, unspoilt villages and charming market towns.

Chatsworth House is one of many fascinating places to visit in this area and adrenaline hunters won't be able to resist Alton Towers. Get outdoors anywhere in this region and you won't be disappointed.

Dovedale near YHA Ilam Hall

For information and to book visit **www.yha.org.uk** or call **0870 770 8868**

Cascade Fountain, Chatsworth House, Derbyshire
britainonview / Martin Brent

River Derwent, Matlock Bath, Derbyshire
britainonview / Dave Porter

Rushup Edge, Derbyshire
www.britainonview.com

Family Facilities

Alstonefield	75	Gradbach	77
Castleton	76	Hartington	78
Crowden	76	Ilam	78
Dimmingsdale	76	Matlock	79
Edale	77	Ravenstor	79
Eyam	77	Youlgreave	80

DERBYSHIRE DALES, PEAKS &
STAFFORDSHIRE MOORLAND

Key
- ▲ Youth Hostel
- ▲ Bunk House
- ▲ Camping Barn
- ☐ Railway Station

NORTH WEST
CITIES &
LAKELAND

YORKSHIRE DALES,
MOORS & COASTLINE

CHESHIRE

STAFFORDSHIRE

STRATFORD &
THE
WELSH BORDERS

SHERWOOD
FOREST &
LINCOLNSHIRE
WOLDS

PEAK DISTRICT

NATIONAL PARK

DERBYSHIRE

Manchester

Crowden

Langsett

Glossop

Edale

Castleton

Abney   Hathersage

Bretton

Whaley Bridge

Chapel-en-le-Frith

Eyam

Dronfield   Eckington

Ravenstor

Buxton

Sheen

Taddington

Bakewell

Chesterfield

Staveley

Bolsover

Underbank

Nab End

Gradbach Mill

Middleton
By Youlgreave   Youlgreave

Birchover

Matlock

Clay Cross

Hartington Hall

Butterton B

Butterton A   Alstonefield

Alstonefield

Matlock Bath

Wirksworth

Alfreton

Ripley

Shining Cliff

Belper

Ilam Hall

Ashbourne

Heanor

Ilkeston

Dimmingsdale

Long Eaton

Derby

Sudbury

Melbourne

NOTTINGHAM
EAST MIDLANDS

Swadlincote

National Forest

Sheffield City

© Oxford Cartographers / 96162
E & OE
Tel: +44 (0) 1865 882884
Email: info@oxfordcarto.com

Derbyshire Dales, Peaks and Staffordshire Moorlands

Alstonefield   B

Gypsy Lane, Alstonefield, nr Ashbourne, Derbyshire DE6 2FZ
Tel: 0870 770 5670

Alstonefield is a delightful village set in rolling hills criss-crossed by the limestone walls typical of the area. Here, are two inter-connecting barns, each with en-suite rooms and a dining/kitchen area. The large garden is perfect for families and small groups looking for a rural escape. Chatsworth House and Alton Towers are both less than an hour's drive away, as are market towns Leek, Ashbourne and Bakewell. It's self-catering only but there are two pubs that serve food within easy walking distance.

Accommodation: 20 beds: 5x4-bed rooms, all en-suite.

By arrangement

Bakewell F

Fly Hill, Bakewell, Derbyshire DE45 1DN
Tel: 0870 770 5682

In a quiet residential part of this historic market town, this is a handy base for exploring the Peak District. The Chatsworth Estate, Haddon Hall, Lathkill Dale and Monsal Dale plus the White and Dark Peak's best walking and cycling areas are all within easy reach. Bakewell's famous puddings are a real treat and with a market tradition stretching back 700 years, there's plenty of things to see. Enjoy freshly cooked meals on-site or walk to one of the many pubs and restaurants in town.

Accommodation: 28 beds: 2x2- and 4x6-bed rooms.

8.00-10.00am
5.00-10.30pm

Bretton F

Bretton, nr Eyam, Hope Valley, Sheffield, Yorkshire S32 5QD
Tel: 0870 770 5720

A cosy hillside property tucked away from it all in the heart of the Peaks. An open fire and coal-burning stove help create a friendly atmosphere. Walkers can escape the crowds without having to get into their cars. Our smallest and highest property in the Peaks is also popular with families and small groups. It's self-catering only but there's a country pub that does food virtually on your doorstep. Alternatively, the historic plague village at Eyam, with shops, pubs and restaurant is only two miles away.

Accommodation: 18 beds: 1x4-, 1x6-, and 1x8-bed rooms.

8.00-10.00am
5.00-10.00pm

Derbyshire Dales, Peaks and Staffordshire Moorlands

Castleton   C

Castleton, Hope Valley, Derbyshire S33 8WG
Tel: 0870 770 5758

YHA Castleton is a 13th Century hall and vicarage in the middle of the village square at the base of Peveril Castle. It's popular with families and walkers who like to explore above and below ground as it's within walking distance of four famous caverns; Blue John, Peak, Treak Cliff and Speedwell. The location also offers easy access to fine walking routes around the valley, overlooked by the spectacular Winnats Pass and imposing Mam Tor. Eat in or visit the many pubs, cafes and shops.

Accommodation: 134 beds: all 2-, 4-, 6- and 8-bed rooms, half of which are en-suite.

           7.00am - 11.00pm

Crowden Awaiting star rating classification F

New building for 2007!

Crowden-in-Longdendale, Glossop, Derbyshire SK13 1HZ
Tel: 0870 770 5784

Situated next to Crowden Brook why not use this newly re-built accommodation and activity centre as an excellent overnight stop when walking the Pennine Way. It's also a great base for walking the surrounding high plateaus and moors. There's plenty to do within easy reach. Glossop with its Railway Centre and splendid Viaduct is well worth a visit. In the evenings eat in at our restaurant, or try the pub at Tintwistle.

Accommodation: 32 beds: 8x4-bed rooms.

                8.00-10.00am 5.00-10.30pm

Dimmingsdale E

Oakamoor, Stoke-on-Trent, Staffordshire ST10 3AS
Tel: 0870 770 5876

A modern, purpose-built woodland property, it's ideal for individuals or small groups looking to explore the Staffordshire Moorlands or for visiting the charming market towns of Ashbourne, Uttoxeter, Cheadle and Leek. Adrenalin junkies stay overnight to beat the queues at Britain's biggest theme park, Alton Towers, just two miles away. For walkers and cyclists there's the Staffordshire Way, Cauldon Canal and several nature reserves. It's self-catering only but there's plenty of eating out in Cheadle.

Accommodation: 20 beds: 2x6- and 1x8-bed rooms

           8.00-10.00am 5.00-10.30pm

For information and to book visit **www.yha.org.uk** or call **0870 770 8868**

Derbyshire Dales, Peaks and Staffordshire Moorlands

Edale F

Rowland Cote, Nether Booth, Edale, Hope Valley, Derbyshire S33 7ZH
Tel: 0870 770 5808

A dedicated YHA Activity Centre offering action packed excitement for all ages. Nestled against the lower slopes of Kinder Scout in the Peak District, it offers courses at all levels from novice to instructor, for families, individuals and groups. Activities offered include; climbing, abseiling, kayaking, canoeing, caving, orienteering, high ropes, hill walking and archery. Great food is served at this very popular location.

Accommodation: 157 beds: mostly 2-8- plus 2x12-bed rooms; 8 en-suite.

                 7.00am - 11.00pm

Eyam C

Hawkhill Road, Eyam, Hope Valley, Derbyshire S32 5QP
Tel: 0870 770 5830

This Victorian folly resembles a tiny, turreted castle perched on the hillside overlooking the historic hamlet of Eyam. Two thirds of the village's population was wiped out during the Great Plague in the 17th Century, and you can trace the tale as you wander around the cottages, parish church and museum. On the boundary of the contrasting White and Dark Peak, there's varied array of excellent walking. YHA Eyam has limited self-catering facilities so why not sample our delicious home-cooked meals?

Accommodation: 60 beds: 4x2-, 6x4-, 2x6- and 1x10-bed rooms and 1x6-bed en-suite.

                 7.30-12.00am 5.00-11.00pm

Gradbach Mill E

Gradbach, Quarnford, Buxton, Derbyshire SK17 0SU
Tel: 0870 770 5834

A former mill in its own secluded grounds on the banks of the River Dane, YHA Gradbach is a superb base for walking the Peaks or the Staffordshire Moorlands. Climbers will love the gritstone Roaches three miles away and there are great family walks in Macclesfield Forest. The National Trust has several properties nearby such as Quarry Bank Mill, Little Morton Hall, Tatton Park, Dunham Massey and Biddulph Grange, while Alton Towers is less than 15 miles away.

Accommodation: Main house 66 beds: 3x2-, 9x4- and 4x6. Farmhouse: 19 beds: 2x2-, 1x3-, 2x6- (1 en-suite) bedded rooms.

               7.00am - 11.00pm

Derbyshire Dales, Peaks and Staffordshire Moorlands

Hartington Hall

  **A**

Hartington, Buxton, Derbyshire SK17 0AT
Tel: 0870 770 5848

A magnificent 17th Century manor house with log fires, oak panelling and a bedroom where Bonnie Prince Charlie once slept. The accommodation is of a high standard and with many smaller rooms, and even a luxury suite, it's ideal for couples and families as well as individuals. Local attractions include Alton Towers, Chatsworth, Pooles Cavern, cycling on the Tissington and Manifold trails and walking in Dovedale. There's great home-cooked food, a children's pets' area and adventure playground too.

Accommodation: 133 beds: 5x1-, 3 double, 4 twin, 4x3-, 9x4-, 3x5-, 2x6-, 1x7-, and 4x8- bed rooms. (19 fully en-suite).

               7.00am - 11.00pm

Hathersage

  F

Castleton Road, Hathersage, Hope Valley, Derbyshire S32 1EH
Tel: 0870 770 5852

Hathersage is a bustling Derbyshire village popular with climbers, walkers and cyclists. It has historic links with Robin Hood's sidekick, Little John, and Charlotte Brontë's Jane Eyre. On the edge of the National Park, it is overlooked by Stanage Edge and on the White Peak Way circular walk. Labybower, Howdon and Derwent reservoirs are a short drive away, as are Chatsworth House and Haddon Hall. Accommodation and a full meals service is provided in a large Victorian house on the edge of town.

Accommodation: 43 beds: 1x2-, 1x3-, 2x4- and 5x6-bed rooms

     7.00-10.00am 5.00-11.00pm

Ilam

 D

Ilam Hall, Ilam, Ashbourne, Derbyshire DE6 2AZ
Tel: 0870 770 5876

A stay in this huge Victorian Gothic manor house is one you won't forget in a hurry. Owned by the National Trust, the hall sits in 84 acres of country park land on the banks of the River Manifold, offering the chance to enjoy this beautiful place without even having to set foot outside the front gates. Popular with families, groups and large parties, it is a great base to explore Dovedale or cycle along the Tissington, Manifold or High Peak trails. There's also a very good restaurant on-site. Parking at NT car park only.

Accommodation: 139 beds: 1x2-, 1x3-, mostly 4-8-, 1x11- and 1x14-bed rooms, some en-suite.

               8.00am - 11.00pm

For information and to book visit **www.yha.org.uk** or call **0870 770 8868**

Derbyshire Dales, Peaks and Staffordshire Moorlands

Langsett **F**

Langsett, Stocksbridge, Sheffield S36 4GY
Tel: 0870 770 5912.

A perfect retreat for people wanting to explore the thousands of acres of High Peak moorland that surround this rural property. The hills rise above 540 metres, before descending down into the Derwent Valley with its spectacular Howden, Derwent and Ladybower reservoirs. It's self-catering only here but there's a pub providing meals and a cafe in the village. Alternatively, visit nearby Holmfirth the quaint setting for long-running TV comedy 'Last of the Summer Wine'.

Accommodation: 27 beds: 4x4-, 1x5- and 1x6-bed rooms.

8.00-10.00am
5.00-10.30pm

Matlock **D**

40 Bank Road, Matlock, Derbyshire DE4 3NF
Tel: 0870 770 5960

Or Smedley's Memorial Hydropathic Hospital as it was once known, it now offers a welcome place to recover after a busy day's exploring. The Heights of Abraham, Gulliver's Kingdom, Chatsworth House and Crich Tramway Village are nearby attractions, while Alton Towers and the American Adventure are also close by. Children are welcome here. There are toddler-friendly facilities and a menu for the under-10s with great food for grown ups too or you'll find plenty of pubs and restaurants in town.

Accommodation: 52 beds: 3x1-, 4x2-, 2x3-, 5x4-, 1x6- and 1x9-bed rooms.

7.30-10.00am
1.00-10.30pm

Ravenstor **★★★ F**

Millers Dale, Buxton, Derbyshire SK17 8SS
Tel: 0870 770 6008

This National Trust property set in 60 acres of magnificent grounds at the confluence of Tideswell and Millers Dale high above the River Wye is perfect for relaxing breaks. If you are interested in hiking, there is plenty on offer here without ever having to get in the car. The fully-licenced restaurant also serves home-cooked local produce, so you don't have to wander far from this haven of peace and relaxation but there is a local pub if you fancy a walk.

Accommodation: 77 beds: 2x2-, 2x3-, 4x4-, 1x5-, 1x6-, 2x7-, 2x8-, 1x10- bed rooms.

7.00am -
11.00pm

Derbyshire Dales, Peaks and Staffordshire Moorlands

Shining Cliff `F`

Jackass Lane, nr Ambergate, Derbyshire DE56 2RE
Tel: 0870 770 8868

YHA Shining Cliff is tucked away on a hillside in the Derwent valley, eight miles south of the historic spa towns of Matlock and Matlock Bath. Set in the heart of open ancient woodland it provides a great base for exploring the nearby Peak District but is also handy for Crich Tramway Museum, Derwent Valley World Heritage Site at Cromford and the world famous Denby Pottery. Or why not try to find the Lullaby Tree on one of our many woodland walks? It's self-catering only and you're advised to bring a torch as we're 10-minutes walk from the parking area.

Accommodation: 22 beds: 1x2-, 2x4- and 2x6-bed rooms.

Youlgreave ★★★ `E`

Fountain Square, Youlgreave, near Bakewell, Derbyshire DE45 1UR
Tel: 0870 770 6104

YHA Youlgreave is the village's former co-op store and retains many original features such as windows inscribed with the shop's services and rooms named after various departments. High above the River Bradford, it enjoys lovely views across the valley and White Peak and is close to the stone circles at Arbor Low and Birchover and the Victorian flourmill and craft centre at Rowsley. It's also handy for Chatsworth and Haddon Hall. There's good food on offer or a pub in the village.

Accommodation: 42 beds: 1x2-, 5x4-, 2x6- and 1x8-bed rooms.

Sheen `C`

Peakstones, Sheen, Derbyshire SK17 0ES
Tel: 01298 84501

Converted from a gritstone barn this well equipped bunkhouse is situated in a quiet corner of the Peak District. With easy access to the Dove and Manifold valleys, Alton Towers and near towns of Buxton, Leek and Bakewell this is a good location for families and groups alike.

Derbyshire Dales, Peaks and Staffordshire Moorlands

Abney ☒

Booking: 0870 770 8868
Arrival number: 01433 650481

Near Hathersage, in the small village of Abney, 1,000 ft up on the gritstone hills at the head of Abney Clough. A good base for walking and climbing, Stanage and Curbar edges are nearby. The moors round about are noted for their fine viewpoints. Sleeping accommodation is in two separate areas and there is a cooking area.

OS 110
GR 198798

Alstonefield ☒

Booking: 0870 770 8868
Arrival number: 01335 310349

Near the picturesque village of Alstonefield, in the heart of the Peak District between Dovedale and Manifold Valley, the barn enjoys fine views of the surrounding limestone hills and is an ideal base for walkers, cyclists and riders. It is also convenient for Alton Towers and visiting historic houses. The barn has a communal cooking area with picnic bench seating, toilet basin and a separate sleeping area upstairs.

OS 119
GR 125569

Birchover ☒

Booking: 0870 770 8868
Arrival number: 01629 650245

This field barn is on a beef farm at the edge of Birchover, between Bakewell and Matlock. Nearby is Stanton Moor with it's Nine Ladies stone circle. There are tables in the communal areas. The cooking shelter, with stone bench, is adjacent and separate showers and toilets are in the farmyard. Minimum booking of five people. The barn is on a campsite.

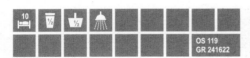

OS 119
GR 241622

Butterton A ☒

Booking: 0870 770 8868
Arrival number: 01539 304185

Perched high above the Manifold Valley, Waterslacks Barn is a secluded base from which to enjoy the limestone valleys and delightful villages of the southern Peak District. The barn has sleeping and communal areas. Campfires allowed, wood is available from the owner.

OS 118/119
GR 087561

Butterton B ☒

Booking: 0870 770 8868
Arrival number: 01539 304185

Wills Barn is a short walk out of Butterton village and lies beside the minor road between Butterton and Wetton Mill. The Manifold and Dove Valleys are nearby. The barn has communal areas with table, benches and cooking area. Camp fires allowed, wood available from owner.

OS 118/119
GR 083564

Edale ☒

Booking: 0870 770 8868
Arrival number: 01433 670273

This field barn at Cotefield Farm overlooks the famous Mam Tor, at the heart of this popular walking area and at the start of the Pennine Way. The high moorland of Kinder and the wooded Derwent Valley are readily accessible. There is a small communal living area with a table and benches. Adjoining the barn, but with external access, is a cooking area and separate toilet.

OS 110
GR 132869

Derbyshire Dales, Peaks and Staffordshire Moorlands

CAMPING BARN

Middleton-by-Youlgreave [X]

Booking: 0870 770 8868
Arrival number: 01629 636746

This barn is part of a working farm on the edge of the small village of Middleton-by-Youlgreave. It is a good base for walking in Bradford Dale and Lathkill Dale, an area full of wildlife interest. The sleeping accommodation is on the first floor, with access via external stone steps. There is a communal living area, and a separate cooking area on the ground floor. The toilet is in an adjacent building. Well behaved dogs on leads accepted, as this is a working farm.

OS 119
GR 196634

Nab End [X]

Booking: 0870 770 8868
Arrival number: 01298 83225

In one of the quieter parts of the Peak District National Park, Nab End lies between Hollinsclough and Longnor. The upper valley of the River Dove, the boundary between limestone and gritstone, is nearby and the river's source, high on Axe Edge lies to the north west. The sleeping and living areas are on the first floor. The ground floor has a washroom/toilets and a kitchen.

OS 119
GR 077662

Taddington [X]

Booking: 0870 770 8868
Arrival number: 01298 85730

The barn is in the centre of the village of Taddington, at over 1,000 ft, midway between Buxton and Bakewell. Surrounded by limestone hills and dales, there are excellent walks and fine views in all directions. There are tables and benches in the communal area, a cooking area, toilets and a metered shower and heater. No dogs please. Pub in the village.

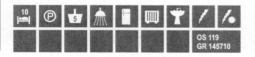

OS 119
GR 145710

Underbank [X]

Booking: 0870 770 8868
Arrival number: 01260 227229/227266

This barn is part of Blaze Farm, a dairy farm near the western edge of the Peak District National Park. It overlooks the Wildboarclough Valley and is close to the well known viewpoint of Shuttlingsloe. The sleeping area is on the first floor, with the living area, kitchen, toilet and shower below. Blaze Farm has an ice-cream parlour and tea room for snacks throughout the day. Breakfast can also be requested.

OS 118
GR 973677

Private Family Rooms

YHA Edale

YHA Hartington Hall

Family rooms are comfortable bunk bedded rooms with washbasin, bed-linen and duvets. Rooms are available for families with children aged three or over. Many have en-suite facilities, some with double beds and meals are usually available, with special menus for children under ten. You can come and go with your own key giving you access throughout the day to facilities including the self-catering kitchen.

From only
£35
per room per night

Yorkshire Dales, Moors and Coastline

The picturesque vale of York divides the Yorkshire Dales in the west of the region from the North York Moors to the east. Each region has its own distinctive natural beauty in this, Britain's largest county.

Beach and seaside attractions are popular with families and the coastline with its characteristic cliffs and sweeping sands offers a fascinating heritage.

Whitby Harbour

For information and to book visit **www.yha.org.uk** or call **0870 770 8868**

Limestone Pavement, Malham Cove
britainonview / Martin Brent

York Minster

Castle Howard, North Yorkshire
www.britainonview.com

Family Facilities

Boggle Hole	87	Malham	90
Grinton Lodge	87	Mankinholes	90
Hawes	88	Osmotherley	90
Haworth	88	Scarborough	91
Helmsley	88	Stainforth	91
Ingleton	89	Whitby	91
Kettlewell	89	York	92
Lockton	89	York (Racecourse)	92

Yorkshire Dales, Moors and Coastline

Beverley Friary ★★★ D

Friar's Lane, Beverley, East Yorkshire HU17 0DF
Tel: 0870 770 5696

A restored Dominican friary cited in the Canterbury Tales, this historic building sits in a quiet corner of this thriving Yorkshire town, near to the renowned Minster and elegant Georgian and Victorian terraces. Markets are held each Saturday. Founded by St John of Beverley at the beginning of the 8th Century, the Minster has notable gothic arches, nave and wooden carvings. There's also easy access from here to Hull, York, the Yorkshire Wolds and the coast too. Fresh, local produce used in all our meals, dinner available if booked in advance.

Accommodation: 34 beds: 1x5-, 1x13- and 1x16- bed rooms.

8.00-10.00am
5.00-11.00pm

Boggle Hole ★★★ C

Mill Beck, Fylingthorpe, Whitby, North Yorkshire YO22 4UQ
Tel: 0870 770 5704

This beautiful converted mill and annexe in a steep ravine running down to the sea, is close to Robin Hood's Bay and a pleasant walk away from Whitby. The sandy bay below was once a notorious smugglers' haunt but now all ages enjoy beachcombing, searching for fossils and exploring rock pools. It's completely surrounded by the North Yorkshire Moors and Pickering with its steam train and trout fishing lakes are only 30 minutes drive away. Fresh food is available on the premises or one mile from local pubs in Robin Hood's Bay.

Accommodation: 80 beds: 4x2-, 14x4-, 1x6-, 1x10-bed rooms.

8.00-10.00am
1.00-11.00pm

Grinton Lodge ★★★★ B

Grinton, Richmond, North Yorkshire DL11 6HS
Tel: 0870 770 5844

This stunning, refurbished shooting lodge sits high on the south facing slopes of Swaledale on the Herriot Way route. The Coast-to-Coast walk passes within a mile of the front door and it is also handy for the Yorkshire Dales Cycleway. Richmond, with its castle and cobbled streets, is only 10 miles away while other attractions to visit include; Kisdon, Wainwath and Aysgarth Falls as well as the Buttertubs and Hardraw Force in Wensleydale. Great food is served on the premises.

Accommodation: 71 beds: 3x2-, 1x3-, 7x4-, 3x6- and 2x8-bed rooms.

7.30-10.00am
5.00-11.00pm

Yorkshire Dales, Moors and Coastline

Hawes

Lancaster Terrace, Hawes, North Yorkshire DL8 3LQ
Tel: 0870 770 5854

Overlooking Wensleydale, with magnificent views of the surrounding fells, this property is on the Pennine Way and ideal for exploring the Yorkshire Dales and Herriott Country. Hawes is a busy market town, famous historically for making rope and with lots going on. The creamery that makes Wensleydale cheese is here and there are plenty of antique shops. The dale itself is well known for its wooded hills and waterfalls, the best known being Aysgarth Falls and Hardraw Force.

Accommodation: 52 beds: 6x2- (2 en-suite), 3x3-, 1x4-, 2x6-, 1x7-, 1x8-bed rooms.

8.00-10.00am
5.00-10.00pm

Haworth

Longlands Drive, Lees Lane, Haworth, Keighley, West Yorkshire
BD22 8RT. Tel: 0870 770 5858

This Victorian mansion overlooks the busy village of Haworth on the wild Pennine moors. The location was made famous by the Brontë sisters, who lived and wrote at the parsonage - now a museum. Walkers will enjoy the Brontë Way, leading to Top Withens, allegedly Heathcliff's farm in Wuthering Heights. Other local attractions include the Keighley and Worth Valley Steam Railway, children's museum Eureka!, in Halifax and the National Museum of Photography, Film and Television in Bradford.

Accommodation: 94 beds: 1x2-, 1x3-, mostly 4-8- plus 1x10- and 1x12-bed rooms.

7.30am -
11.00pm

Helmsley

Carlton Lane, Helmsley, York, North Yorkshire YO62 5HB
Tel: 0870 770 5860

Located in one of the prettiest country towns in North Yorkshire, this cosy stonewalled property with comfortable modern facilities is just a few minutes away from the shops, pubs and 13th Century castle. Exploring the moors on foot or by bike is a definite option from here and there are also many places of historic and cultural interest to visit like; Duncombe Park, Nunnington Hall and Rievaulx Abbey to name but a few. In the evenings, eat in or head out to one of the many excellent pubs.

Accommodation: 35 beds: mainly 4- and 6-bed rooms. Plus 1x3-bed en-suite room.

10.00-12.00am
5.00-10.00pm

For information and to book visit **www.yha.org.uk** or call **0870 770 8868**

Yorkshire Dales, Moors and Coastline

COUNTRYSIDE

COUNTRYSIDE

COUNTRYSIDE

Ingleton ★★★★ D

Sammy Lane, Ingleton, Carnforth, Lancashire LA6 3EG
Tel: 0870 770 5880

Whether or not you are attempting the 25-mile lung-busting Three Peaks Challenge up Pen-y-Ghent, Whernside and Ingleborough, a stay at this renovated Victorian house in private grounds will restore your spirits. There are some more sedate walks nearby, including a Waterfalls Walk to Thornton Force or tours of White Scar Caves. There's excellent limestone climbing too and Ingleton village is delightful and has many charming pubs and places to eat. Children love the park next door too.

Accommodation: 58 beds: 4- and 6-bed rooms.

 7.00-10.00am 5.00-11.00pm

Kettlewell ★★★ D

Kettlewell, Skipton, North Yorkshire BD23 5QU
Tel: 0870 770 5896

Perhaps best known in recent times as the setting for the Calendar Girls film, Kettlewell is a small Upper Wharfedale village half-an-hour north of Skipton. Surrounded by the limestone pavements and lush green Dales, Kettlewell is a haven for climbers and walkers. YHA's base is an old stone house in the centre and provides easy access to some of the finest parts of the Dales, the Embsay Steam Railway, Skipton Castle and Bolton Abbey. Sample finest Dales produce in our restaurant.

Accommodation: 40 beds: 1x2-, 1x4-, 2x5- and 4x6-bed rooms.

  8.00-12.00am 5.00-10.30pm

Lockton ★★★★ 🚶 B

Old School, Lockton, Pickering, North Yorkshire YO18 7PY
Tel: 0870 770 5938

Located in the heart of the North Yorkshire Moors National Park, this former village school is packed with 'green' features to minimize its environmental impact. Nearby Dalby Forest is full of trails that are perfect for little legs while high-level walks on the Moors, the city of York and the coast are also easily accessible. Levisham Station on the North York Moors Steam Railway is a short distance away so you can combine a linear walk from base with a train ride back. Self-catering only.

Accommodation: 21 beds: 1x4-, 1x8- and 1x6- and 1x3-bed rooms.

  8.00-10.00am 5.00-10.00pm

Yorkshire Dales, Moors and Coastline

Malham   D

Malham, Skipton, North Yorkshire BD23 4DE
Tel: 0870 770 5946

Families love this modern, comfortable property in the heart of a beautiful Dales village and surrounded by classic limestone scenery. Malham Cove, Malham Tarn and Gordale Scar are all within a short walk. The Pennine Way and Yorkshire Dales Cycle Way pass close by, making it very popular with walkers and cyclists too. Visit Janet's Foss waterfall or try and spot the peregrine falcons against the limestone scar at the Cove. Good wholesome Yorkshire produce is cooked and served here daily.

Accommodation: 82 beds: 1x2-, 4x4-, 1x5- and 9x6-8-bed rooms.

7.00-10.00am
5.00-11.00pm

Mankinholes   C

Mankinholes, Todmorden, Lancashire OL14 6HR
Tel: 0870 770 5952

This listed Yorkshire manor house dates back to the 17th Century and has been refurbished to create a high standard of self-catering accommodation on the Pennine Way. The area is rich in walking trails and within easy reach of Haworth, a working steam railway and Eureka!, the interactive children's museum in Halifax. The nearby Hollingworth Lake Water Activity Centre offers rock climbing, orienteering, sailing, canoeing/kayaking, windsurfing and power boating.

Accommodation: 32 beds: 2x2-, 4x4- and 2x6-bed rooms

8.30-10.00am
5.00-10.30pm

Osmotherley   F

Cote Ghyll, Osmotherley, Northallerton, North Yorkshire DL6 3AH
Tel: 0870 770 5982

Nestling between the Cleveland and Hambleton Hills on the western edge of the North York Moors, Osmotherley is a picture postcard village. YHA offers accommodation in a former mill, half a mile down a secluded lane in an unspoilt valley. A range of excellent walking and cycling routes pass through here. Mount Grace Priory, the famous Rievaulx Abbey or the World of James Herriot are worth a look. The cluster of pubs around the village cross makes a good evening out after a good, hearty meal in.

Accommodation: 72 beds: 1x2-, 2x3-, 1x4- and 5x6-bed rooms, some en-suite.

7.00-11.00am
5.00-10.30pm

For information and to book visit **www.yha.org.uk** or call **0870 770 8868**

Yorkshire Dales, Moors and Coastline

Scarborough

Burniston Road, Scarborough, North Yorkshire YO13 0DA
Tel: 0870 770 6022

There's plenty to do during a stay at this beautiful 17th century water mill, two miles from Scarborough. Good food, miles of great walking and cycling plus beaches galore ensure families and outdoor enthusiasts love this place in equal measure. The property offers the best of both worlds sited in a quiet, riverside location but close to the nearby Sea Life Centre and only a 20 minute walk to the sea. Why not visit Scarborough Castle, go boating at Peasholm Park or visit the Stephen Joseph Theatre, home of the playwright Sir Alan Ayckbourn.

Accommodation: 48 beds: 3x4- and 6x6-bed rooms.

          7.00-10.00am 5.00-11.30pm

Stainforth

Stainforth, Settle, North Yorkshire BD24 9PA
Tel: 0870 770 6046

In this pretty Dales village, this beautiful Georgian house in wooded gardens offers plenty of reasons to stay. The river Ribble and The Ribble Way footpath pass close by and there's a good variety of other walks to suit all abilities, including the three great Yorkshire peaks. The Settle to Carlisle Railway starts two miles away or visit the excellent Falconry Centre. Eat great food in-house or visit Skipton with its lively markets, canal, castle, great pubs and legendary pork pies - 20 minutes away.

Accommodation: 47 beds: 1x2-, 2x4-, 2x6-, 1x7-, 1x8- and 1x10-bed rooms, some en-suite.

                7.00-12.00am 3.00-10.30pm

Whitby

New YHA for 2007!

Abbey House, East Cliff, Whitby, North Yorkshire YO22 4JT
Tel: 0870 770 6088

Right on the headland, 199 steps up from the cobbled quayside and smack next door to the famous ruined Abbey sits Abbey House, YHA's new home in Whitby. The views of the Esk Valley and surrounding coastline are to die for, as is the brand new, fully-refurbished accommodation. Relax in the historic gardens or spend a day on one of the nearby sandy beaches. Explore the nearby moors on foot or bike before sitting down to fine food, in our restaurant.

Accommodation: 100 beds: 2x2-, 3x3-,9x4-, 1x5-, 6x6-, and 1x10 bed rooms.

              7.00am - 10.30pm

Yorkshire Dales, Moors and Coastline

York ★★★ D

Water End, Clifton, York, North Yorkshire YO30 6LP
Tel: 0870 770 6102

The ancient walled city of York has always attracted visitors, some more welcome than others. The Romans, Anglo-Saxons, Vikings and Normans have all left today's tourists with plenty to see. Our comfortable Victorian house, a stroll along the River Ouse from the centre, is the perfect place to stay. Climb Clifford's Tower or the magnificent Minster, take a ghost tour or visit the fantastic National Railway Museum or the Jorvik Viking Centre. Great food and drink in-house and great night-life in the city.

Accommodation: 150 beds: mostly 4-bed rooms, plus 4x6- and 3x8-bed options. Premium 1-, 2-, 3- and 4-bed rooms.

24 hours

York Racecourse ★★★ A

 New YHA for 2007!

Tadcaster Road, York YO1 7EN
Tel: 01904 620911

Overlooking the famous racecourse, this modern two-storey centre is just a few minutes drive, or a good stroll, from the walled city centre and its many attractions. Visit the excellent National Railway Museum, the famous Minster or the Jorvik Viking Centre. York's 365 pubs make for a bustling night-life and there are some excellent shops and restaurants here too. All rooms are small and private with most en-suite. Cafeteria-style catering is available. Breakfast is included in the price and evening meals and packed lunches are available for pre booked groups.

Accommodation: 130 beds: 12x1-, 21 x 2-4- & 2x6-bed rooms.

by arrangement

Bishopdale C

The Old School Bunkhouse, Bishopdale Valley, Thoralby, Leyburn, North Yorkshire DL8 3TB
Tel: 01969 663856

Centrally located for walks and attractions, the Herriot Way, Aysgarth Falls, Bolton Castle, Wharfedale, Wensleydale and Swaledale and nearby towns of Hawes, Richmond and Leyburn. The bunkhouse has been refurbished to a high standard with an attractive open-plan lounge and dining area, and a modern kitchen. The Street Head Inn, lies 150 metres away & provides a warm welcome and varied lunch and evening menu. Breakfast by prior arrangement, served at the Inn.

BBQ

Access by arrangement

For information and to book visit **www.yha.org.uk** or call **0870 770 8868**

Yorkshire Dales, Moors and Coastline

Brompton on Swale

Booking: 0870 770 8868
Arrival number: 01748 818326

This former byre, in the farmyard of Village Farm, is in the picturesque village of Brompton-on-Swale itself. It is an excellent stop-off point for the Coast to Coast Walk, which is just half a mile away at Catterick Bridge. The historic town of Richmond is just three miles away. The first floor has sleeping accommodation in three rooms, with toilet and shower. On the ground floor there are lounge, dining and kitchen areas. Washing and drying facilities are available on request. Pub and shop 100m.

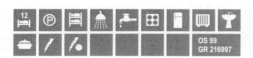

OS 99
GR 216997

Farndale

Booking: 0870 770 8868
Arrival number: 01751 433053

In the farmyard of Oak House in the North York Moors National Park, this barn has wonderful views over High Farndale. It is one and a half miles from the Coast to Coast walk, three miles from the Cleveland Way and two miles from the Lyke Wake Walk. There are also many local walks including the well-known Farndale Daffodil Walk. One bag of logs is provided per night for the woodburner, additional bags can be bought. Breakfast is available by prior arrangement. Parking is limited to four cars. No dogs please.

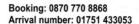

OS 94
GR 659986

Kildale

Booking: 0870 770 8868
Arrival number: 01642 722135

This former barn and wheelhouse is a listed building in the farmyard at Park Farm. It is in the North York Moors National Park and the Cleveland Way is on the doorstep, as are many good local walks. Kildale station on the Esk Valley Railway is just one mile away. Sleeping accommodation is in the first floor loft. The two toilets and two showers are in an adjacent building.

OS 94
GR 602085

Lovesome Hill

Bookings: 0870 770 8868
Arrival number: 01609 772311

This former corn store is in the farmyard at Lovesome Hill Farm. Centrally placed for exploring the Yorkshire Dales and the North York Moors National Parks, the barn is just 200 yds from the Coast to Coast Walk. The bustling market town of Northallerton is just four miles away. Sleeping accommodation is in bunks on the first floor, with two toilets on the ground floor. Small groups can book breakfast by arrangement. Sheets and duvets for hire, provisions can be ordered in advance.

OS99
GR 361998

Low Row

Booking: 0870 770 8868
Arrival number: 01748 884601

This barn is on Low Whita Farm, an outstanding location in Swaledale, at the heart of the Yorkshire Dales National Park. It is just one mile from the Coast to Coast Walk plus there are many local walks including the 'Corpse Road' running between Keld and Reeth. Sleeping accommodation, with bunk beds and mattresses, is on the top floor. On the ground floor there is a dining area.

OS 92
GR 003983

Richmond

Booking: 0870 770 8868
Arrival number: 01748 822940

These three former byres, at East Applegarth Farm, have magnificent views across Swaledale. It is a great base for exploring the Yorkshire Dales National Park, with many scenic local walks and the Coast to Coast path passing 50 yards away. Sleeping accommodation is in two rooms with pillows, sleeping bags and mattresses provided.

OS 92
GR 135017

Yorkshire Dales, Moors and Coastline

Sinnington ☒

Booking: 0870 770 8868
Arrival number: 01751 473792

This former granary is on the family-run Cliff Farm. Enjoy local walks, visit the steam railway, take a day trip to Flamingoland or the North York Moors and coast. The first floor sleeps nine, and the ground floor sleeps three, single mattresses provided. The toilets, shower and washing facilities are in an adjacent building. Ideal for winter use. Breakfasts are available, please book in advance.

OS 94
GR 752849

Westerdale ☒

Booking: 0870 770 8868
Arrival number: 01287 660259

This former byre, with lovely views of Westerdale Moor and Castleton Rigg, is in the farmyard at Broadgate Farm in the North York Moors National Park. The numerous local walks include the Rosedale Circuit, and within three miles are the Coast to Coast and Lyke Wake Walks. Sleeping accommodation is in two ground floor rooms.

OS 94
GR 671049

Camping Barns

There are many Camping Barns in the YHA network owned and operated by farmers in fantastic rural locations.

Alstonefield

Abney

Trawden

from only
£6
per night!

Facilities vary but typically offer a place to prepare food, cold water, sleeping platforms and a flush toilet. You'll need a sleeping bag, torch, warm clothes and walking boots or wellies. See the individual camping barn entries for details on facilities.

Tel: 0870 770 8868 or email: campingbarns@yha.org.uk

CAMPING BARN

Fantastic Member Benefits!

While you no longer need to be a member to stay with YHA, your membership card is great value and provides discounts as well as a passport to a worldwide network of 4,000 destinations.

White Horse, Uffington, Oxfordshire
britainonview / Martin Brent

Tower of London
www.britainonview.com

Please check the terms & conditions of any offers before using. Discounts and offers are provided by third parties and may include a right to withdraw the offer.

Discounts on travel, insurance, gym membership, high street and on-line purchases and tourist attractions are available to you as a YHA member.
Visit: www.yha.org.uk

Tel: 0870 770 8868 www.yha.org.uk

North West Cities and Lakeland

Chester, Manchester and Liverpool make great city break destinations with their theatres, museums, art galleries, shops and nightlife.

For outdoor pursuits and quiet relaxation, the Lake District National Park is one of the UK's most beautiful places and home to England's highest mountain. Stay in one of YHA's remote Lakeland properties and say goodbye to the hustle and bustle of the 21st Century.

Ashness Bridge, Lake Distr
britainonview / Rod Edwa

For information and to book visit **www.yha.org.uk** or call **0870 770 8868**

...oss Ullswater, from near Martindale, Lake District
ainonview / Rod Edwards

Old Trafford, Manchester
britainonview / Martin Brent

Liverpool

Family Facilities

Ambleside	99	Grasmere BH	105
Arnside	99	Hawkshead	105
Birdoswald	100	Kendal	106
Borrowdale	100	Keswick	107
Buttermere	101	Lakeside	107
Chester	101	Langdale	107
Coniston		Liverpool	108
Coppermines	102	Manchester	108
Coniston HH	102	Patterdale	108
Derwentwater	103	Slaidburn	109
Dufton	103	Wastwater	109
Ennerdale	104	Windermere	109
Eskdale	104		

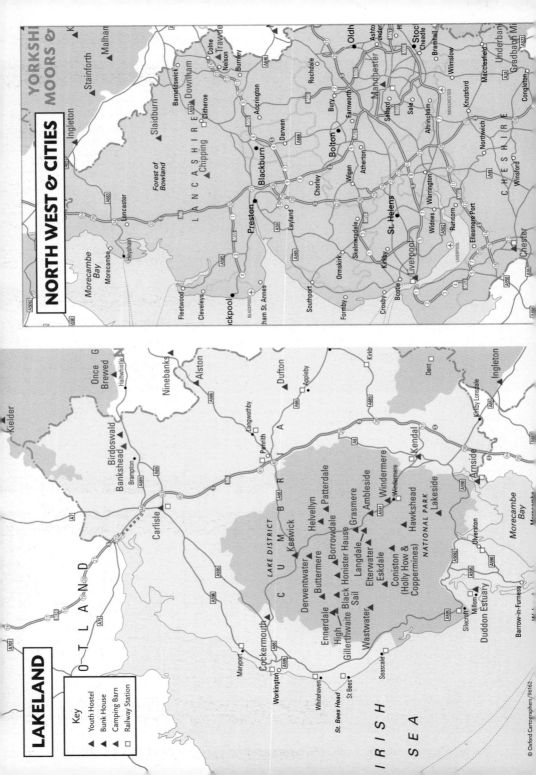

LAKELAND

Key
- ▲ Youth Hostel
- ▲ Bunk House
- ▲ Camping Barn
- □ Railway Station

NORTH WEST & CITIES

© Oxford Cartographers /96162

Alston C

The Firs, Alston, Cumbria CA9 3RW
Tel: 0870 770 5668

This modern property overlooks the South Tyne Valley and is on both the Pennine Way and the Coast-to-Coast cycle route. Alston claims to be England's highest market town and sits at 1,000 feet above sea level. The cobbled main street, 17th Century architecture and open views of the wild solitary fells and Pennine moorland make this a very attractive place to stay. Alston is a bustling town, renowned for its delicious locally-made specialties such as Cumberland Mustard and Alston Cheese, so be sure to take advantage.

Accommodation: 30 beds: 2x2-, 2x4- and 3x6-bed rooms.

8.00-10.00am
5.00-10.30pm

COUNTRYSIDE

Ambleside A

Waterhead, Ambleside, Cumbria LA22 OEU
Tel: 0870 770 5672

Right on the edge of Lake Windermere, looking over the water to the Langdale Pikes sits YHA Ambleside. On the edge of a bustling village with plenty of shops, two cinemas, attractions, pubs and restaurants, it is popular with watersports, walking and climbing enthusiasts. It also provides a great base for the less active who may prefer travel by steamboat to the many nearby places of interest. Eat in and sample great local food or try a night out in town or at the cinema.

Accommodation: 252 beds: 47x2-5- and 18x6-8-bed rooms.

7.15am -
11.45pm

COUNTRYSIDE

Arnside C

Redhills Road, Arnside, Cumbria LA5 0AT
Tel: 0870 770 5674

This large Edwardian house looks over Morecambe Bay and the Lakeland fells. Arnside is quieter than many Lake District villages. Morecambe Bay has extraordinary tides and quicksands but its beauty and wildlife, viewed from this glorious spot are unforgettable. A great touring base for the Lakes and the western Yorkshire Dales. Sample local dishes in our comfortable restaurant or there's a pub close by.

Accommodation: 72 beds: all 1-8-bed rooms.

7.30-11.30am
5.00-10.30pm

COAST

North West Cities and Lakeland

Birdoswald

Birdoswald Roman Fort, Gilsland, Carlisle CA8 7DD
Tel: 0870 770 6124

Birdoswald is a Roman Fort on Hadrian's Wall near Gilsland in Cumbria. We provide self-catering accommodation in a converted farm building that forms part of the visitor centre complex for this impressive archaeological site. Most components of a Roman Frontier System have been preserved here in a relatively compact area. A visit to the fort is included in the price but the surrounding, picturesque area, including a mile of the best preserved sections of wall, is hugely popular with walkers.

Accommodation: 36 beds: 2x8-, 2x6- and 2x4-bed rooms.

8.00-10.00am
5.00-10.30pm

Black Sail

Black Sail Hut, Ennerdale, Cleator, Cumbria CA23 3AY
Tel: 07711 108450

Remote, and accessible only on foot, this is the kind of property that lovers of wild places dream about. Walkers with a sense of adventure return often for the superb access to Great Gable, Pillar, Red Pike and Steeple to name but a few of the nearby peaks. You'll be glad of our hearty home-cooked breakfasts and evening meals using local ingredients and recipes.

Accommodation: 16 beds: 2x4- and 1x8-bed rooms.

8.00-10.00am
5.00-10.00pm

Borrowdale

Longthwaite, Borrowdale, Keswick, Cumbria CA12 5XE
Tel: 0870 770 5706

This large Lakeland property, in one of the most beautiful valleys in the Lake District, has fine views, a warm informal atmosphere and great food making it popular with families as well as individual guests. Surrounded by mountains, the choice of walks is endless. From low-level family friendly routes to high-level adventure; it's all on the doorstep. Keswick, just seven miles away, has shops, a theatre, and cinema.

Accommodation: 88 beds: mostly 2-, 4- and 6- plus 1x8-bed rooms (two rooms converted for disabled access with shower and toilet opposite).

7.30-10.00am
1.00-10.30pm

For information and to book visit **www.yha.org.uk** or call **0870 770 8868**

North West Cities and Lakeland

Buttermere C

Buttermere, Cockermouth, Cumbria CA13 9XA
Tel: 0870 770 5736

Buttermere is a tranquil haven at the foot of the Honister pass. Crummock Water and Lake Buttermere offer plenty of opportunities for boating, diving and canoeing or walk from the front door onto Red Pike or High Stile. Afterwards, enjoy home-cooked food and admire breathtaking views from our comfortable lounge, or take a half-mile stroll into Buttermere village, where there are two small hotels.

Accommodation: 70 beds: 1x2- but mostly 4-6-bed rooms.

COUNTRYSIDE

Carlisle ★★★ A

Old Brewery Residences, Bridge Lane, Caldewgate, Carlisle CA2 5SR
Tel: 0870 770 5752

Accommodation in this former Brewery close to the city centre, is only open in July and August. The legacy of the history of this border town is all around and the Tullie House Museum and Art Gallery are both a short walk away. Travel to Settle on the steam railway for unforgettable views. There's no restaurant at YHA Carlisle but everything from pavement cafes, to the finest cuisine, are right on the doorstep.

Accommodation: 56 beds: single beds in flats for up to 7 people.

CITY

Chester ★★ F

40 Hough Green, Chester, Cheshire CH4 8JD
Tel: 0870 770 5762

Ideal for a city break with great countryside on your doorstep, this large comfortable Victorian house is just a mile from the city centre. Go walking through medieval streets and shopping galleries, boating on the River Dee or visit Chester Zoo. The Boat Museum and Aquarium at Ellesmere Port, Jodrell Bank Science Centre and even the castles, coast and mountains of north Wales are easily accessible. Chester abounds with great places to eat out and the nearby theatre has opera, dance and drama. Breakfast included. Meals available to pre-booked groups.

Accommodation: 117 beds: all 2-10-bed rooms.

CITY

North West Cities and Lakeland

Cockermouth

Double Mills, Cockermouth, Cumbria CA13 0DS
Tel: 0870 770 5768

On the banks of the River Cocker this 17th Century watermill is a 10-minute walk from the centre of this attractive market town. As it is self-catering only, sample good food in the nearby pubs and restaurants. Poet William Wordsworth, Fletcher Christian who led the mutiny on 'The Bounty' and John Dalton, the world renowned atomic scientist, were born here or nearby and you too will be inspired by the town's charm and easy access to the quieter western fringes of the Lakes.

Accommodation: 26 beds: 1x4-, 1x10- and 1x12-bed rooms.

7.30-10.00am
5.00-10.30pm

Coniston Coppermines

Coniston, Cumbria LA21 8HP
Tel: 0870 770 5772

Ever had a mountain in your back garden? This charming property gives you a 500 foot head start on the ascent of the Old Man of Coniston and you will be bowled over by the splendid views and walking options nearby. You will probably choose to eat in as access is via an unsurfaced track, descending a mile to Coniston village with a supermarket and four pubs that serve real ales and good food. Just make sure you've packed a torch for the walk home.

Accommodation: 26 beds: 3x4-, 1x6- and 1x8-bed rooms

7.00-11.00am
5.00-10.00pm

Coniston Holly How

Far End, Coniston, Cumbria LA21 8DD
Tel: 0870 770 5770

This traditional Lakeland house is just minutes from the main village and Coniston Water. All levels of walking routes are nearby; sail or canoe on the lake; try pony-trekking or some of the best mountain bike trails in the country. Cruise the lake, visit Brantwood, former home of John Ruskin or discover 'Wildcat Island' of Swallows & Amazons fame. The village has shops and several pubs. Our hearty home-cooked evening meals will bring you back to life after a long busy day.

Accommodation: 60 beds: 4x4-, 4x8- and 1x12-bed rooms.

7.30-10.00am
5.00-10.30pm

For information and to book visit **www.yha.org.uk** or call **0870 770 8868**

North West Cities and Lakeland

Derwentwater   B

Barrow House, Borrowdale, Keswick, Cumbria CA12 5UR
Tel: 0870 770 5792

This 200-year old mansion by the shores of Derwentwater has extensive grounds, stunning views and even its own waterfall. With woodlands and a large grassy area children soon fall in love with this place. There's a selection of spectacular walks or relaxing strolls for all ages. Nearby Keswick has all the facilities of an attractive bustling market town. YHA Derwentwater is renowned for its homemade food with local specialities for evening meals.

Accommodation: 88 beds: mostly 4-8-, 1x10- and 1x22-bed rooms.

8.30am - 10.30pm

Duddon Estuary ★★★  D

Borwick Rails, Millom, Cumbria LA18 4JU
Tel: 0870 770 6107

This is heaven for birders, botanists walkers and cyclists with a stunning panorama of the Lake District fells. A long sandy beach is a short walk away from the garden. The southern Lake District fells, Muncaster Castle, the World Owl Trust Centre, Ravenglass and Eskdale Narrow Gauge Steam Railway and the South Lakes Wild Animal Park are within easy reach. For groups of friends, schools, educational parties and families wanting to self-cater, this is a great place to relax or get active - the choice is yours.

Accommodation: 18 beds: 1x2- and 2x8-bed rooms.

8.00-10.00am
4.00-10.00pm

Dufton ★★★★ C

Dufton, Appleby, Cumbria CA16 6DB
Tel: 0870 770 5800

This large stone house on the green in the pretty village of Dufton is a great base for exploring the surrounding wild moorland and green valleys. The Pennine Way is on the doorstep and you can approach Cross Fell or High Cup Nick from here. Eat in and enjoy the antics of red squirrels in the garden. Cyclists enjoy miles of traffic-free lanes. It's handy for the famous Appleby Horse Fair in June or the Appleby Jazz Festival in July, a stay at YHA Dufton doesn't have to be quiet.

Accommodation: 32 beds: 2x2-, 5x4- and 1x8-bed rooms.

8.30-10.00am
5.00-10.00pm

North West Cities and Lakeland

Elterwater   D

Elterwater, Ambleside, Cumbria LA22 9HX
Tel: 0870 770 5816

This converted farm is in the heart of a village enormously popular with walkers, cyclists and climbers exploring some of the Lake District's most dramatic scenery including Little and Great Langdale, Pavey Ark and Harrison Stickle. A ramble along the river to Skelwith Force is also a must. YHA Elterwater is comfortable, warm and friendly and offers great home cooked food made from local produce. The excellent Britannia Inn and village shop are also close by as are organised outdoor activities of all kinds.

Accommodation: 40 beds: 6x2-, 1x4- and 4x6-bed rooms.

8.00-10.00am
5.00-10.30pm

Ennerdale   F

Cat Crag, Ennerdale, Cleator, Cumbria CA23 3AX
Tel: 0870 770 5820

Two converted forestry cottages in the heart of a remote wooded valley, are a haven for those escaping the hustle and bustle. It's even powered by its own hydroelectric turbine and offers everything you need from home-cooked meals to comfortable beds. Surrounded by fells, ridges and famous peaks to challenge the adventurous, there are sheltered, forest tracks for families and cyclists. There's also canoeing, rock climbing, orienteering and scrambling at the Field Centre next door.

Accommodation: 24 beds comprised of 3x4- and 2x6-bed rooms.

7.30-10.30am
5.00-11.00pm

Eskdale ★★★ F

Boot, Holmrook, Cumbria CA19 1TH
Tel: 0870 770 5824

Set in its own extensive grounds, YHA Eskdale is very child-friendly and popular with families and walkers. There are local walking routes for all abilities, idyllic trails and the Ravenglass and Eskdale Steam Railway winds the 10 miles from Boot village to the coast. Eskdale Mill, Burnmoor stone circles, Stanley Gyll Falls and The World Owl Centre are nearby. Great family meals are on offer here and the nearest shop is two miles away. The nearest pub is a five-minute walk away.

Accommodation: 49 beds: 8x2-6-,1x8- and 1x7- bed rooms.

8.00-10.00am
5.00-10.30pm

For information and to book visit **www.yha.org.uk** or call **0870 770 8868**

North West Cities and Lakeland

Grasmere Butharlyp Howe ★★★★ A

Easedale Road, Grasmere, Cumbria LA22 9QG
Tel: 0870 770 5836

Surrounded by high-level ridge and fell walks, Grasmere's natural beauty and outdoor activities attract many visitors. Butharlyp Howe is a traditional Victorian house with extensive grounds, a safe play area for children and plenty of outdoor games. It also offers outdoor activities including watersports, climbing, orienteering and cycling. There's a fantastic home-cooked bistro-style menu on offer while the village is renowned for its gingerbread and attractive shops.

Accommodation: 80 beds: 5x2-, 8x4-, 2x5-, 2x6-, 1x8- and 1x10-bed rooms.

Grasmere Thorney How ★ F

Easedale Road, Grasmere, Cumbria LA22 9QG
Bookings c/o YHA Grasmere Butharlyp Howe. Tel: 0870 770 5836

Thorney How is a former rustic farmhouse and more than 350 years old. It nestles in a secluded spot 15 minutes walk from Grasmere village with virtually no passing traffic. Ideal for walkers, there are routes to suit all levels of ability from hikes into the hills to nine local lakes and tarns for those wanting shorter expeditions. Eat with us and discover why we have a reputation for delicious hearty, healthy balanced meals for adults and children.

Accommodation: 49 beds: 3x4-, 1x5-, 2x2- and 2x6- and 2x9-bed rooms.

Hawkshead ★★★ C

Hawkshead, Ambleside, Cumbria LA22 0QD
Tel: 0870 770 5856

This Grade II listed Regency-style mansion overlooks tranquil Esthwaite Water. It's a gorgeous spot from which to explore surrounding Beatrix Potter country. An ideal place for a family holiday, Grizedale forest is on our doorstep with some of the best mountain biking Britain can offer. Splendid home-cooked food is available or the village, with shops and pubs is a mile away.

Accommodation: 109 beds: 14x3-4- and 8x6-8-bed rooms.

North West Cities and Lakeland

Helvellyn

Greenside, Glenridding, Penrith, Cumbria CA11 0QR
Tel: 0870 770 6110

900 feet above sea level and a mile from the nearest village, a stay here is a treat for those getting away from it all. You can climb Helvellyn (3,116 ft) via the vertiginous Striding Edge or climb aboard a restored 19th Century steamer for a cruise on Ullswater or visit the spectacular 60 ft waterfall at Aira Force on Gowbarrow Fell, particularly after heavy rain. Enjoy our delicious home-cooked food at the end of a long day.

Accommodation: 60 beds: mostly 2-4- and 2x6-bed rooms.

7.30-10.30am
5.00-10.30pm

Honister Hause

Seatoller, Keswick, Cumbria CA12 5XN
Tel: 0870 770 5870

Steep valleys stretch from the mountains down to the shores of Derwentwater creating one of the most beautiful and distinctive landscapes in the British Isles. This former quarry workers' house at the summit of Honister Pass is in true mountain country with easy access to England's highest peaks. Visit the Slate Mine (next door), still working after 400 years. The nearby villages offer pubs and restaurants or enjoy an evening in and sample our hearty home-cooked meals.

Accommodation: 26 beds: all 2-4-bed rooms.

7.30-10.00am
5.00-11.00pm

Kendal

118 Highgate, Kendal, Cumbria LA9 4HE
Tel: 0870 770 5892

The market town of Kendal is the 'Gateway to the Lakes', an ideal stopover point and an excellent base to explore the Lake District and the Yorkshire Dales National Parks. This attractive Georgian townhouse in the town centre is part of an arts complex with a cinema, gallery and café. Walk along the River Kent, visit Sizergh Castle and Levens Hall with its famous topiary gardens. Windermere and the heart of the Lakes is little more than a 15 minute drive away and Morecambe Bay less than half an hour away. Meals are available to pre-booked groups.

Accommodation: 48 beds: 4x2-, 1x3-, 2x4-, 3x6-, 1x11-bed rooms.

7.30-10.00am
1.00-10.30pm

For information and to book visit **www.yha.org.uk** or call **0870 770 8868**

North West Cities and Lakeland

Keswick   A

Station Road, Keswick, Cumbria CA12 5LH
Tel: 0870 770 5894

Looking over the river to mountains and only minutes from Keswick's popular town centre, this recently refurbished accommodation is a great place to stay. You can try watersports and hire mountain bikes, or shops nearby sell everything you could possibly need to enjoy the great outdoors. After one of our delicious evening meals, enjoy a performance at the theatre by the Lake, or browse in local galleries. There's a leisure centre for wet days as well as a climbing wall and a museum.

Accommodation: 85 beds: 1x2-, 7x3-, 7x4-, 2x5 and 4x6- bed rooms.

             7.00am-11.00pm

Lakeside Awaiting star rating classification D

Lakeside, Newby Bridge, Ulverston Cumbria LA12 8BD
Tel: 01539 539012

This superb location in the very heart of the Lakes on the edge of Windermere is ideal for families, small and large groups and individuals. There's a good range of accommodation options set in a mile and a half of woodland on the western shore. Sample the stunning walking country on your doorstep or use the centre as an ideal base to explore the Lake District. Food and shops can be found on-site or unwind with pleasant lakeside walks. Meals are available if booked in advance.

Accommodation: 250 beds, 1-8 bedded rooms, some en-suite.

                 24 Hours

Langdale ★ F

High Close, Loughrigg, Ambleside, Cumbria LA22 9HJ
Tel: 0870 770 5908

This Victorian mansion stands in several acres of grounds between Elterwater and Grasmere. With log fires and many original features, it has long been popular with walkers, climbers, cyclists and educational groups for its easy access to some of the finest walking country and valleys in the Lakes. Great local food is on offer in the restaurant. Spend the summer evenings on our balcony overlooking great views or in front of a real fire on cool nights.

Accommodation: 96 beds: 2x2-, 2x3-4-, 7x5- and 4x11-bed rooms.

                7.00-10.00am 5.00-11.00pm

North West Cities and Lakeland

Liverpool ★★★★   A

25 Tabley Street, off Wapping, Liverpool, Merseyside L1 8EE
Tel: 0870 770 5924

Bright, modern, en-suite bed and breakfast accommodation by the Albert Dock, this is an excellent base for exploring the thriving arts and fascinating heritage of this festival city. Galleries, museums and The Beatles Story are a stroll away and the city centre is just a 10-minute walk. With numerous live music venues, clubs, cabarets and bars ranging from the traditional to the designer, you'll be glad of YHA Liverpool's comfortable beds to fall into at the end of a hectic day.

Accommodation: 100 beds: all 3-, 4- and 6-bed en-suite rooms.

   24 hours

Manchester ★★★★ A

Potato Wharf, Castlefield, Manchester, M3 4NB
Tel: 0870 770 5950

Football, fine museums, nightlife and fabulous shops, a stay at YHA Manchester with its buzzing waterside setting will be a city break to remember. The city offers a huge choice of restaurants, cinemas, concert halls, museums and theatres. And YHA Manchester's en-suite, family and premium rooms mean there's accommodation to suit everyone. Book in for home-cooked food in the restaurant by the canal at the end of a hectic day.

Accommodation: 136 beds: 30x4-, 2x5- and 3x2-bed rooms, all en-suite.

   24 hours

Patterdale ★★ F

Patterdale, Penrith, Cumbria CA11 0NW
Tel: 0870 770 5986

This Scandinavian-style building in a quiet location is an ideal base for families, individuals and groups to explore the many surrounding ridges and fells. The energetic will want to climb nearby Helvellyn, while those seeking more gentle pursuits can cruise on an Ullswater steamer, hire a boat, or mountain bike nearby. There's a sport massage clinic based on the premises. Home cooked food is on offer, pubs in the village and more cafes and restaurants in nearby Glenridding. Please note: children must be over five to stay here.

Accommodation: 82 beds: 3x2-, 7x8- and 2x10-bed rooms.

           8.30-12.00am 1.00-10.00pm

North West Cities and Lakeland

Slaidburn
 ★★★ E

King's House, Slaidburn, Clitheroe, Lancashire BB7 3ER
Tel: 0870 770 6034

In an unspoilt village, isolated and protected by surrounding fells, this refurbished 17th Century inn has an open fire, beamed ceilings and cosy atmosphere. Quiet roads, cycle paths and walking routes traverse the surrounding moorland. Close to Settle and the Yorkshire Dales, or short drive from the Lake District, YHA Slaidburn is self-catering only, but a nearby pub and a café serve food.

Accommodation: 30 beds: 1x3-, 4x4-, 1x5- and 1x6-bed rooms.

           8.00-10.00am 5.00-10.30pm

Wastwater
★★★ D

Wasdale Hall, Wasdale, Seascale, Cumbria, CA20 1ET
Tel: 0870 770 6082

This stunning half-timbered property has grounds that stretch down to the shores of Wastwater, England's deepest lake. The sight of Illgill Head and Whin Rigg screes plunging into clear blue water is unforgettable. From here you can also see some of England's highest mountains. Enjoy a relaxing meal with us in our wood panelled dining room after a strenuous day in the fells or visit the Wasdale Head Inn, the 'home of English rock climbing'.

Accommodation: 50 beds: 2x4-, 1x6-, 1x8- and 2x14-bed rooms.

                8.00-10.00am 5.00-10.30pm

Windermere
★★★ B

Bridge Lane, Troutbeck, Windermere, Cumbria LA23 1LA
Tel: 0870 770 6094

In a spectacular location overlooking the lake and mountains, this idyllic countryside setting is only 2 miles from Windermere and its many attractions. Enjoy a lake cruise, a choice of high or low level walks, or a day at the Lake District Visitor Centre or award-winning aquarium. Or simply enjoy our home-cooked meals and panoramic views from the dining room. An ideal location for families, children also love the large wooded grounds with our own Nature Trails.

Accommodation: 69 beds: mostly 4-bed rooms, plus 1x2-, 1x3-, 1x5-, 2x6- and 1x8-bed options.

               7.30-11.00am 1.00-10.30pm

COUNTRYSIDE

North West Cities and Lakeland

Bankshead **X**

Booking: 0870 770 8868
Arrival number: 01697 73198

This converted stone byre on a traditional family-run farm has outstanding views over the Irthing Valley. Ideal for a stopover while walking Hadrian's Wall (bus daily in summer). Bankshead is 4 miles from Brampton and 2 miles from Birdoswald Visitor Centre. Food shopping service - contact the owner 24hrs in advance and food can be bought and stored in the fridge.

OS 86
GR 586649

Chipping **X**

Booking: 0870 770 8868
Arrival number: 01995 61209

A former stable and hayloft opposite the farmhouse, the barn is just ½ mile from Chipping village and an ideal base for group activities. Sleeping accommodation, toilets and a shower are on the first floor with more toilets in the adjacent former pig sty! There is a dining area and separate kitchen. Dryer available. Recreation and children's play area outside. Breakfast is available if booked in advance. Dogs and tents by arrangement. Orienteering, guided walking and a wild boar park nearby.

OS 102
GR 616435

Downham **X**

Booking: 0870 770 8868
Arrival number: 01200 441667 or 07773 245212

A basic field barn on the Downham Estate with stunning views of Pendle Hill, near the picturesque village of Downham. It is close to the Witches Way and the Lancashire Cycleway, two miles from the Pendle Way and two and a half miles from the Ribble Way, providing excellent opportunities for walkers. There is parking across the road from the barn, in a former quarry. Dogs welcome.

OS 103
GR 795445

High Gillerthwaite (Ennerdale) **X**

Booking: 0870 770 8868
Arrival number: 01946 861237

A traditional barn dating back to the 16th Century, in the most remote of the Lakeland valleys, with outstanding views of Pillar and the adjacent fells. Excellent base for fell walking, rock climbing and cycling. On the Coast to Coast walk. There are three sleeping areas on first and second floors. On the ground floor is a sitting room and separate cooking area. There is a bathroom on the ground floor. Evening meals and breakfasts are available if booked in advance.

OS 89
GR 142141

Trawden **X**

Booking: 0870 770 8868
Arrival number: 01282 865257

This recently restored barn is in an idyllic setting surrounded by meadows, one mile from Trawden village. There are plenty of opportunities for walking in the Forest of Trawden and on the South Pennine Moors. The barn has a sleeping gallery with mattresses provided, a sitting area and two bathrooms. In summer, enjoy your meals in the conservatory. There is a TV, garden and pool room with darts and table tennis. Electricity and gas payments should be made direct to the owners.

OS 103
GR 903381

YHA Activity Centres

YHA Activity Centres offer everything from climbing, kayaking and surfing to sailing and gorge scrambling. Whatever you choose our instructors will make sure you have a great time.

from only

£68

for a two-night programme including all activites

All centres are AALA licensed and operate to the highest safety standards. You can stay for as long as you like and prices include all transport, food, specialist equipment and accommodation.

Available at several locations in England and Wales - visit our website for more details.

www.yha.org.uk / Tel: 0870 770 8868

Northumberland, Durham and Hadrian's Wall

The northeast is famous for its wild open spaces and beaches and a rich heritage dating back to Celtic and Roman times. Its bustling cities also offer great shopping, buzzing nightlife and a thriving arts scene. Hadrian's Wall is dotted with Roman forts and St Oswald's Way, the Coast-to-Coast path and the Northumberland National Park all offer superb opportunities for outdoor recreation.

Hadrian's Wall, Northumberland

For information and to book visit **www.yha.org.uk** or call **0870 770 8868**

Lindisfarne Castle

The Angel of the North

Durham

Family Facilities

Edmundbyers   115
Kielder   116
Langdon Beck   116
Ninebanks   117
Once Brewed   117
Wooler   117

NORTHUMBERLAND, DURHAM & HADRIAN'S WALL

Key
- ▲ Youth Hostel
- ▲ Bunk House
- ▲ Camping Barn
- ☐ Railway Station

SCOTLAND

NORTH
Sea

● Berwick-upon-Tweed

Holy I.

Belford

Wooler

Alnwick
● Alnmouth

● Amble

NORTHUMBERLAND
Byrness
● Rothbury

KIELDER
FOREST
Kielder
PARK

NATIONAL PARK

NORTHUMBERLAND

Ashington
● Newbiggin by the Sea
Morpeth
Bedlington
● Blyth

Barrasford
NEWCASTLE
Ponteland
Whitley Bay

Once
Brewed
Grindon
Longbenton
Gosforth
Tynemouth
Birdoswald
Haltwhistle
Hexham
Corbridge
Newcastle
Wallsend
South Shields
Bankshead
Bardon Mill
Blaydon
Jarrow
Gateshead
Boldon
Washington
Ninebanks
Allendale Town
Sunderland
Ryhope
Edmundbyers
Stanley
Houghton le Spring
Consett
Seaham
Chester
le Street
Hetton le Hole
Alston
Durham

Wearhead
Tow Law
Peterlee
Easington Colliery
Stanhope
Crook
Willington
NORTH WEST
CITIES &
LAKELAND
Langdon Beck
Holwick
Spennymoor
Witton
Hartlepool
Bishop Auckland
Dufton
Teesdale
Middleton in Teesdale
Newton Aycliffe
Billingham
Redcar
Saltburn
Eston
Loftus
Stockton-on-Tees
Middlesbrough
Barnard Castle
Darlington
Thornaby-on-Tees
Guisborough
TEESSIDE
Kildale
Westerdale

Richmond
Brompton
On Swale
Lovesome
Hill
Farndale
Osmotherley
Kendal
Low Row
Grinton
Lodge
YORKSHIRE DALES,
MOORS & COASTLINE
Hawes
Helmsley
Bishopdale

Stavar
Hauge
Berger

Kristia
Götebo

Amste

© Oxford Cartographers/96162
E & OE
Tel +44(0) 1865 882884
Email info@oxfordcarts.com

Northumberland, Durham and Hadrian's Wall

Byrness ★★ X

7 Otterburn Green, Byrness, Newcastle-upon-Tyne, Northumberland NE19 1TS. Tel: 0870 770 5740

Byrness is the last village in England before the A68 winds through the Cheviot Hills and into Scotland. YHA Byrness comprises two adjoining Forestry Commission houses that have been converted into a small, simple property that makes an ideal base for exploring this beautiful corner of the Northumberland National Park. After a busy day, enjoy a well-earned rest in the garden where you may be rewarded with a glimpse of a red squirrel or a roe deer. Visitors should stock up in advance as local amenities are limited.

Accommodation: 20 beds: 2x2-, 2x5- and 1x6-bed rooms.

    8.00-10.00am 5.00-10.00pm

Durham ★★★ A

University of Durham, St Chad's College, 18 North Bailey, Durham DH1 3RH. Tel: 0870 770 6072

Founded in 1904, St Chad's College is one of the oldest colleges in the University of Durham and provides B&B accommodation for YHA guests in the holidays. It's right in the heart of this medieval city, next to the magnificent cathedral and is surrounded by stunning architecture. Durham Castle is very close by and another short walk takes you to the marketplace. The open-air museum at Beamish plus Raby Castle and Hadrian's Wall are also easily accessible - as is the bustling night scene.

Accommodation: 168 beds: 87 x 1-, 82 x 2- bedded rooms (all singles and twins).

     8.00am - 12.00pm

Edmundbyers ★★★ D

Low House, Edmundbyers, Consett, Co Durham DH8 9NL; Tel: 0870 770 5810

Edmundbyers is a pretty hamlet surrounded by heather moorland, five miles west of Consett. This 17th Century self-catering property is a former inn on the Sea-to-Sea cycle route but is also popular with walkers and anglers. Sailing and windsurfing are available on the three-mile long Derwent Reservoir, less than half a mile away, which covers 1,000 acres of this Area of Outstanding Natural Beauty. There's a good variety of walking and Hadrian's Wall to see plus the Beamish Museum is only 13 miles away. The local pub offers a wide selection of meals and local beers.

Accommodation: 29 beds: 1x3-, 1x4-, 2x5- and 2x6-bed rooms.

           8.00-10.00am 5.00-10.00pm

COUNTRYSIDE

CITY

COUNTRYSIDE

Northumberland, Durham and Hadrian's Wall

Kielder

   **B**

Butteryhaugh, Kielder Village, Hexham, Northumberland NE48 1HQ
Tel: 0870 770 5898

A stay here illustrates why there are never any water shortages in Northumberland. Kielder is the largest man-made lake in Western Europe with nearly thirty miles of shoreline surrounded by thousands of acres of beautiful forest. You'll stay in the middle of it all in an outdoor enthusiast's paradise. There are cycle trails, walking routes and bird watching sites galore with great sailing, lake cruises and fishing also on your doorstep. Excellent local produce is cooked and served daily in the restaurant.

Accommodation: 41 beds: 2x2-, 2x3-, 2x4-, 1x5- and 3x6-bed rooms.

8.00-12.00am
5.00-7.00pm

Langdon Beck

★★★   **E**

Forest-in-Teesdale, Barnard Castle, Co Durham DL12 0XN
Tel: 0870 770 5910

If phrases like 'ecological footprint' or 'alternative energy source' mean nothing to you, you should stay here at the home of Green Shoots, a YHA scheme that teaches young people to reduce their environmental impact through sustainable living. The solitude of the Forest-in-Teesdale fells is breathtaking and there are magnificent views and walks in every direction - to High Force or Cauldron Snout waterfalls or along a section of the Pennine Way. It's remote but good food is served on-site.

Accommodation: 31 beds: 2x2-, 1x3-, 3x4-, 1x5 ensuite-, 1x7-bedded rooms.

7.00-10.00am
5.00-11.00pm

Newcastle

★★ **B**

107 Jesmond Road, Newcastle-upon-Tyne, Tyne & Wear NE2 1NJ
Tel: 0870 770 5972

Famed for its friendly welcome, the North East's 'capital city' is perfect for a short break. Great shopping and nightlife is guaranteed while the list of existing cultural icons such as the Tyne Bridge and The Angel of the North have recently been added to by trendy new arts venues like The Sage and the Baltic. Older attractions include Hadrian's Wall, Bede's World and Segedunum Roman Fort while the energetic, will find stunning walking and cycling close by on coastal and countryside trails.

Accommodation: 52 beds: 6x2-, 2x4-, 4x6- and 1x8-bed rooms.

7.00am -
11.00pm

For information and to book visit **www.yha.org.uk** or call **0870 770 8868**

Northumberland, Durham and Hadrian's Wall

Ninebanks    D

Orchard House, Mohope, Ninebanks, Hexham, Northumberland NE47 8DQ; Tel: 0870 770 5974

YHA Ninebanks offers a quiet retreat. Originally a 17th Century lead miner's cottage, it stands in the peaceful valley of Mohope Burn in the North Pennines Area of Outstanding Natural Beauty. Walkers can explore secluded countryside and wild moorland, both of which are rich in wildlife, flora, fauna and industrial archaeology. Conveniently near the C2C cycle route and close to Killhope lead mining centre, the A686 (England's most scenic road) and Isaac's Tea Trail. Meals available to pre-booked groups.

Accommodation: 28 beds: 1x2-, 3x4-, 1x6- and 1x8-bed rooms,

     8.00-10.00am 5.00-10.00pm

Once Brewed  C

Military Road, Bardon Mill, Northumberland NE47 7AN Tel: 0870 770 5980

When soldiers visited the neighbouring inn, close to Hadrian's Wall, the ale was so weak, they demanded it be brewed again. However, when teetotaler Lady Trevelyan, opened up this building for YHA in 1936, she said she wanted tea, brewed only once! The Roman wall is a big draw for this property which is just half a mile from one of its most spectacular sections. It's an easy walk to the Vindolanda and Housesteads forts. Don't forget to try our Once Brewed Pale Ale.

Accommodation: 77 beds: mostly 2,3,4-, 1x5-, some 6- and 1x8-bed rooms.

             8.00-10.00am 2.00-10.00pm

Wooler   C

30 Cheviot St, Wooler, Northumberland NE71 6LW Tel: 0870 770 6100

England's most northerly hostel in the foothills of the Cheviots is ideally situated for exploring Northumberland National Park, the Holy Island of Lindisfarne, border castles and fine sandy beaches. St Cuthbert's Way, The Pennine Cycleway and Ravenber Way all pass close by and the area is steeped in archaeology and prehistorical remains. The clear skies offer an ideal base for stargazing and the Market Town has specialist shops, inns, working pottery and much more.

Accommodation: 46 beds: 4x2-, 8x4- and 1x6-bed rooms.

               8.00-10.00am 5.00-10.30pm

Northumberland, Durham and Hadrian's Wall

Grindon - Hadrian's Wall **A**

Military Road, Grindon near Haydon Bridge, Northumberland, NE47 6NQ. Tel: 01434 688668

This converted telephone exchange within yards of Hadrian's Wall provides an excellent base for a quiet get-away. Situated within a World Heritage Site, it offers great walking and cycling as well as horse-riding nearby. You'll find sites of former Roman forts in either direction along the wall - Chesters to the east and Housesteads to the west. Haydon Bridge is just a few miles south down the Tyne Valley. Breakfast is included in the price and meals are available.

Access by arrangement

Barrasford **X**

Booking: 0870 770 8868
Arrival number: Mr Milburn, 01434 681237

This converted stone coach house, now a camping barn, overlooks the North Tyne River. Walkers and cyclists will find it allows easy access to the breathtaking scenery surrounding Hadrian's Wall. For a camping barn, the facilities are very good with light, heat and even a drying room. There is a nearby shop and pub.

OS 87
GR 919733

Holwick **X**

Booking: 0870 770 8868
Arrival number: 01833 640506

Two separate field barns on Low Way Farm near the River Tees, close to High Force on the Pennine Way, with lots of beautiful walks nearby. The larger barn has bunks on the first floor; the smaller one has bunks in two areas on the ground floor. The barns also have worktops in the cooking area, and a sitting area. Meals can be ordered from the Farmhouse café. There is a butcher's shop on the farm.

OS 92
GR 914270

Wearhead **X**

Booking: 0870 770 8868
Arrival number: 01388 537395

This former farmhouse is a listed building, next to a stream on Blackcleugh Farm. Just half mile from the Weardale Way, there are plenty of local walks in the area, and the Killhope Lead Mining Museum is three and a half miles away. The sleeping accommodation and toilet are on the first floor. On the ground floor there is a cooking, eating and sitting area. Coal is available for the open fire, which also heats the water. There is no electricity.

OS 91
GR 851397

Witton **X**

Booking: 0870 770 8868
Arrival number: 01388 488322

A former barn and dairy, this barn is on the Witton Castle Estate, which offers a range of facilities including, public bars, games and television rooms, a shop and a cafeteria (except in winter) in the grounds of the 15th Century castle. The Weardale Way is only half mile away. The 'National Byway' for cyclists passes the barn door. The barn is a single storey building with sleeping accommodation and a cooking/eating area.

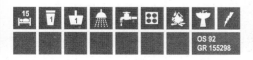

OS 92
GR 155298

Hostelling International

Sydney Harbour, Australia

Look for the Hostelling International symbol to be sure of a safe, clean, comfortable and friendly stay.

Hostelling International has over 4,000 Youth Hostels in more than 80 countries, whether you're embarking on a month's trip to experience Europe or a year's odyssey around the world, you'll find a range of Youth Hostels in the locations you need. In a new country with a different culture and language, you can trust Hostelling International to provide you with a good night's sleep in friendly surroundings at an affordable price.

San Fransisco

Egypt

Welsh Mountains, Moors and Coastline

From Britain's smallest cathedral at St David's to the buzzing modern Millennium Stadium complex in Cardiff, Wales has something for everyone. Delight in Celtic myths about Merlin, see valleys, once home to mines that powered the industrial revolution, or visit one of the 400 castles that criss cross this vast expanse of unspoilt coastline and countryside.

Llynnau Mymbyr, Conwy
britainonview / Steve Lewis

For information and to book visit **www.yha.org.uk** or call **0870 770 8868**

Porth Dinllaen, Gwynedd
britainonview/Wales Tourist Board

Cardiff's shopping district
britainonview / Grant Pritchard

Family Facilities

Anglesey	123	Newport	130
Bangor	123	Pen-y-Pass	130
Betws-y-Coed	123	Poppit Sands	130
Borth	124	Port Eynon	131
Brecon	124	Snowdon	132
Broad Haven	124	St David's	132
Bryn Gwynant	125		
Capel Curig	125		
Capel-y-Ffin	125		
Conwy	126		
Danywenallt	126		
Idwal	127		
Kings	127		
Llanberis	128		
Llanddeusant	128		
Llwyn-y-Celyn	129		
Manorbier	129		
Marloes	129		

For information and to book visit **www.yha.org.uk** or call **0870 770 8868**

Welsh Mountains, Moorland and Coastline

Anglesey Outdoors A

Porthdafarch Road, Holyhead, Anglesey, LL65 2LP
Tel: 01407 769351

This well-equipped YHA makes a great base for exploring Anglesey, a mecca for a whole range of outdoor activities which include climbing, cycling, sea fishing, canoeing and more. YHA Anglesey is situated close to the Anglesey Coast Path and beach and only a short distance from local restaurants. It's also a great location for a stopover for travelling to or from Ireland.

Accommodation: 82 beds: 2-12 bed-rooms.

New YHA for 2007!

 L4R

8.00-10.00am
12.00-10.00pm

Bangor ★★ C

Tan-y-Bryn, Bangor, Gwynedd LL57 1PZ
Tel: 0870 770 5686

This large Victorian house is very close to Bangor centre - a short drive from the mountains of Snowdonia or the beaches on Anglesey. Penrhyn Castle is a 20-minute walk away and the castles of Caernarfon, Beaumaris, Dolwyddelan, Conwy and Harlech are also easily accessible. Bangor Pier stretches halfway across the Menai Strait to Anglesey, or you can cross the bridge to find watersports and beaches galore. Eat in our popular restaurant or the many bars and restaurants nearby.

Accommodation: 70 beds: 1x2-, 3x4-, 6x6- and 2x10-bed rooms.

7.30am -
10.30pm

Betws-y-Coed ★★★★ A

Swallow Falls, Betws-y-Coed, Gwynedd, LL24 0DW
Tel: 01690 710796

Betws-y-Coed sits at the confluence of three valleys in a heavily forested Area of Outstanding Natural Beauty in Snowdonia. It is just two miles from the main village and is part of a very lively tourist complex opposite the Swallow Falls waterfall, one of the loveliest spots in North Wales. It's a great base for walkers, climbers or cyclists. Other attractions nearby include Snowdonia Mountain Railway, Blaenau Ffestiniog Slate Mines, Portmerion, and historic Welsh castles. Café/Bistro and pub on-site.

Accommodation: 78 beds: 3x2-, 9x6-, 3x4- and 1x8-bed rooms.

7.30am -
9.00pm

COAST

COAST

COUNTRYSIDE

Welsh Mountains, Moorland and Coastline

Borth ★★ F

Morlais, Borth, Ceredigion SY24 5JS
Tel: 0870 770 5708

Overlooking Cardigan Bay, 20 metres from a beautiful sandy beach, it's easy to see why this Edwardian house is called Morlais or 'the voice of the sea'. The golden sands shelve very gently - perfect for children - and stretch north for two miles to the Dyfi National Nature Reserve with its fantastic sand dunes and abundant wildlife. Further inland, the world renowned Centre for Alternative Technology is an inspirational experience. Round off the day in our restaurant as the sun sets over the bay.

Accommodation: 60 beds: 5x4-, 4x6- and 2x8- bed rooms.

7.30-10.00am
2.00-10.30pm

Brecon ★★★ C

Groesffordd, Brecon, Powys LD3 7SW
Tel: 0870 770 5718

This imposing former Victorian farm house set half a mile from the village of Groesffordd, is a perfect base for exploring the Brecon Beacons and Black Mountains. There are many great walks and cycle routes nearby, and Llangors Lake is only four miles away for canoeing, sailing and pony trekking. The bustling market town of Brecon is just three miles away, with its quaint cobbled streets, imposing cathedral and lively farmer's market. There are plenty of family rooms, some en-suite. The hostel specialises in using local produce to provide a delicious and extensive food menu.

Accommodation: 53 beds: all 2-10-bed rooms, some en-suite.

7.30- 11.00am
5.00-10.30pm

Broad Haven ★★★ D

Broad Haven, Haverfordwest, Pembrokeshire SA62 3JH
Tel: 0870 770 5728

This modern property has sweeping views of St Bride's Bay and is just minutes from a lovely sandy beach with rock pools. At low tide you can walk the half-mile across the beach to Little Haven, a tiny village with quaint fishermen's cottages and quayside. Try sea kayaking, surfing, canoeing, windsurfing, scuba diving or just walk along the Pembrokeshire Coastal Path. Visit St David's, take a boat trip to Skomer Island or Oakwood Theme Park at Narberth. Eat well in or out - the choice is yours.

Accommodation: 77 beds: mostly 4-, 5- and 7-bed rooms, plus 1x2-bed room, most en-suite.

7.30-10.00am
3.00-10.00pm

For information and to book visit **www.yha.org.uk** or call **0870 770 8868**

Welsh Mountains, Moorland and Coastline

Bryn Gwynant

Nantgwynant, Caernarfon, Gwynedd LL55 4NP
Tel: 0870 770 5732

Experience the stunning beauty of Snowdonia from an early Victorian mansion set next to a lake in 40 acres of wooded grounds. With stunning views over Llyn Gwynant and Snowdon, good food and a warm welcome, you may not want to venture far. Walkers of all ages can take the Watkin path up Snowdon, which begins less than a mile away, while the Cambrian Way is even closer. For wet days, there's an interesting time to be had at the Sygun Copper Mine between Llyn Gwynant and Beddgelert.

Accommodation: 73 beds: mainly 2-, 3-, 4-, 5- and 6-bed rooms, with 1x8-, 1x9- and 1x10-bed option.

8.00-10.00am
5.00-11.00pm

Capel Curig

Plas Curig, Capel Curig, Betws-y-Coed, Conwy LL24 0EL
Tel: 0870 770 5746

In the centre of this small, bustling village, the spectacular views of Moel Siabod and the Snowdon Horseshoe leave you itching to get your walking boots on. Scale the mountains, wander through the forest or stroll along the River Llugwy. Try something new at the Plas-y-Brenin Outdoor Activity Centre with its dry ski slope and climbing walls or go canoeing on the nearby lake and river. We offer hearty home-cooked meals for groups of 10 or more who book in advance or there are pubs in the village.

Accommodation: 52 beds: mostly 2-, 4- and 5-bed rooms, plus 1x6- and 1x8-bed option.

7.00-12.00am
5.00-10.30pm

Capel-y-Ffin

Capel-y-Ffin, Llanthony, nr Abergavenny, Monmouthshire NP7 7NP
Tel: 0870 770 5748

Situated high up on the Gospel Pass eight miles south of Hay-On-Wye, this former hill farm looks out across the Black Mountains. A magnet for adventurers, walkers and cyclists, with easy access to the Cambrian Way and Offa's Dyke trails. Hay-on-Wye with its many bookshops and Abergavenny's museum, art galleries and tapestry is 14 miles south. No mobile phone signal, no TV but a warm welcome and delicious food.

Accommodation: 38 beds: 1x3-, 1x4-, 1x6-, 1x8- and 1x18/20-bed rooms.

7.30-10.00am
5.00-10.00pm

For information and to book visit **www.yha.org.uk** or call **0870 770 8868**

Welsh Mountains, Moorland and Coastline

Cardiff ★★★ E

2 Wedal Road, Roath Park, Cardiff CF23 5PG
Tel: 0870 770 5750

Next door to Roath Park, two miles from the city centre, YHA Cardiff is great for exploring the stylish, cosmopolitan Welsh capital. Visit the Millennium Stadium, the only British sports venue with a retractable roof, Cardiff Castle or St Fagan's National History Museum. There's great shopping and lots of smart places to eat and drink around the recently revamped Cardiff Bay area. There are pubs close by as well as a whole host of night-spots in the city. Meals available to pre-booked groups.

Accommodation: 66 beds: 3x4-, 3x6-, 1x8- and 2x14-bedded rooms.

            7.00am - 11.00pm

Conwy ★★★ A

Larkhill, Sychnant Pass Road, Conwy LL32 8AJ
Tel: 0870 770 5774

YHA Conwy is an ideal base for exploring North Wales. A great location for families, youth organisations or anyone wanting easy access to the coastal resorts and Snowdonia. The hostel is situated on a hill just outside the town walls with panoramic views of Conwy Castle and the harbour. The town centre with its pubs, tea shops and local attractions is a 10 minute walk away. The castle is well worth a visit and the quayside is great for sitting back and watching the yachts and fishing boats go by.

Accommodation: 80 beds: 2- and 4-bed rooms, en-suite showers.

                8.00-12.30am 2.00-10.30pm

Danywenallt ★★★ C

Talybont-on-Usk, Brecon, Powys LD3 7YS
Tel: 0870 770 6136

Stunning and secluded, this converted Welsh farmhouse in the Brecon Beacons has many en-suite rooms and is ideal for families or small groups. There are lovely views of the hills with direct access to many walks surrounding the reservoir and the nearby ridges. Take a leisurely boat cruise on the Monmouth and Brecon Canal, sail at Llangorse Lake or explore the hills by bike or pony. No self-catering here but local produce and regional flavours dominate our fine menu and breakfast is included.

Accommodation: 36 beds: 1x2-, 3x3-, 5x4- and 1x5-bed rooms. Most rooms have private facilities.

            8.00-12.00am 5.00-10.30pm

For information and to book visit **www.yha.org.uk** or call **0870 770 8868**

Welsh Mountains, Moorland and Coastline

Ffynnon Wen

Awaiting star rating classification | X

Ty Nant, Cerrigydrudion, Conwy LL21 ORH
Tel: 01490 420349

Ffynnon Wen is situated within the Hiraethog area of North Wales, on the edge of Snowdonia National Park. A traditional farmhouse and bunkhouse providing excellent facilities it's set in eight acres of land and offers a fantastic base for activities including walking, fishing, white water rafting, horseriding and much more. Meals made from fresh ingredients produced at Ffynnon Wen or sourced locally are available.

Accommodation: 36 beds: 2x2-, 4x6+- bed rooms.

8.00-10.30am
5.00-10.00pm

Idwal Cottage

★★★★ | A

Nant Ffrancon, Bethesda, Bangor, Gwynedd LL57 3LZ
Tel: 0870 770 5874

Stay in the environmentally conscious property situated in the impressive Ogwen Valley between the Glyder and Carneddau mountains. It is perfectly placed for strolls to see Rhaeadr Ogwen Waterfalls, Cwm Idwal nature reserve (with its dramatic lake) and Devil's Kitchen. This self-catering accommodation is ideal to stay at if you are doing the Cambrian way or the Welsh 3000. Being the oldest YHA property in Wales, Idwal Cottage has retained the character and charm well-known throughout the years while providing excellent modern accommodation and facilities.

Accommodation: 37 beds: mostly small and medium-sized rooms.

8.00-10.00am
5.00-10.00pm

Kings

★★ | F

Kings, Penmaenpool, Dolgellau, Gwynedd LL40 1TB
Tel: 0870 770 5900

This country house and annexe sit by a river, five miles from the pretty town of Dolgellau in southern Snowdonia. With fine views of Cader Idris and just a stone's throw from the Mawddach Estuary and Barmouth's beaches, it will delight hill walkers, beachcombers and wildlife enthusiasts alike. Forget TV and mobile phones, just relax. Mountain bikers will enjoy some of the best terrain in the UK and there's pony trekking, watersports and fishing in Dolgellau. Breakfast available. Meals available to pre-booked groups.

Accommodation: 42 beds: all 6-bed rooms. (4 en-suite).

8.00-10.00am
5.00-10.30pm

For information and to book visit **www.yha.org.uk** or call **0870 770 8868**

Welsh Mountains, Moorland and Coastline

COUNTRYSIDE

Llanberis ★★★ C

Llwyn Celyn, Llanberis, Caernarfon, Gwynedd LL55 4SR
Tel: 0870 770 5928

The views of Snowdon's summit will tempt the most reluctant to get up there, even if it is via the mountain railway from Llanberis! For the more energetic, mountain bikers, climbers and walkers will be spoilt for choice. Llyn Padarn offers fishing, canoeing, windsurfing and sailing, or you can have a go at pony trekking. Nearby are eight blue flag award beaches - ideal for the kids (big and little). Fresh home-cooked meals are served here or there are plenty of alternatives in Llanberis.

Accommodation: 50 beds: 4x2-, 4x4-, 3x6- and 1x8-bed rooms, 2 fully en-suite with double beds.

              8.00-11.00am 5.00-10.00pm

COUNTRYSIDE

Llanddeusant ★★★ F

The Old Red Lion, Llanddeusant, Carmarthenshire SA19 9UL
Tel: 0870 770 5930

As YHA properties go, this is one of our most remote. A former 18th Century inn, it's seven miles from the nearest shops at Llangadog in an unspoilt corner of the Brecon Beacons. But with its location comes spectacular and inspiring views of the Sawdde Valley an irresistible temptation for walkers and cyclists. Trails lead up to the legendary Llyn-y-Fan glacial lake and a mile away there's a red kite feeding station. It's self-catering only here, but there is a pub a mile away.

Accommodation: 26 beds: 3x4-, 1x6- and 1x8-bed rooms.

         8.00-10.00am 5.00-10.00pm

COUNTRYSIDE

Llangollen ★★★ F

Tyndwr Road, Llangollen, Denbighshire LL20 8AR
Tel: 0870 770 5932

Tyn Dwr Hall is a large Victorian manor and coach house set in seven acres of private grounds. It specifically caters for groups that come to take part in the many adventure activities on offer at the centre as well as visiting local attractions including the canal, steam railway and the horseshoe falls and pass. The superb range of activities on offer at the centre include gorge walking, climbing, canoeing, mountain biking and a high ropes course.

Accommodation: 134 beds: 2-, 4- and 6-bed rooms, with several 10-20-bed options.

                8.00-10.00am 3.00-10.00pm

For information and to book visit **www.yha.org.uk** or call **0870 770 8868**

Welsh Mountains, Moorland and Coastline

Llwyn-y-Celyn   C

Libanus, Brecon, Powys LD3 8NH
Tel: 0870 770 5936

This cosy 18th Century farmhouse sits overlooking the river Tarell in 15 acres of ancient woodland with views towards Y Gyrn. Popular with hill walkers and families wanting to unwind, the Brecon Beacons Visitor Centre is just down the road and offers guided walks and specialist courses in mountain safety in the summer. At the end of the day, relax and sample local Brecon Brewery ales while watching sheep on the hill opposite, then tuck into our tasty home-cooked food.

Accommodation: 41 beds: 5x2-, 3x4-, 1x5-, 1x6- and 1x8-bed rooms.

8.00-10.00am
5.00-11.00pm

Manorbier D

Manorbier, nr Tenby, Pembrokeshire SA70 7TT
Tel: 0870 770 5954

Manorbier is on the coast between Pembroke and Tenby and has a lovely sandy beach, popular with surfers and perfect for children. We are based on a cliff-top in a futuristic former Ministry of Defence building. Popular with groups and families, it offers easy access to the beach, coastal path and many local attractions. Oakwood Theme Park, Wedlock Dinosaur Park and Pembroke and Carew Castles are all close by. There's great food on offer here if you choose to eat in.

Accommodation: 69 beds: 1x2-, 1x3-, 5x4-, 6x6- and 1x8-bed rooms.

7.30-10.00am
5.00-10.30pm

Marloes Sands   Farmhouse (Hostel) Cowshed (Bunkhouse)   F

Runwayskiln, Marloes, Haverfordwest, Pembrokeshire SA62 3BH
Tel: 0870 770 5958

Marloes is a beautiful, isolated stretch of sand with great rock pools at low tide. This cluster of National Trust farm buildings has exceptional sea views towards Skomer, Skokholm and Gateholm Islands - you can even walk out to Gateholm at low tide! The islands are also home to many reefs and wrecks making them very popular with divers and a boat trip from Martin's Haven to see the gannet colony is a must. This is a self-catering only property, but there are shops and pubs nearby.

Accommodation: 26 beds: 1x2-, 2x4-, 1x6- and 1x10-bed rooms.

8.00-10.00am
5.00-10.30pm

Welsh Mountains, Moorland and Coastline

Newport D

Lower St Mary Street, Newport, Pembrokeshire SA42 0TS
Tel: 0870 770 6072

This converted Victorian school offers self-catering accommodation in the bustling Welsh seaside village of Newport. As well as fine coastal walks, a short journey inland takes you into the Preseli Mountains, where there are wild ponies and plenty of quiet unspoilt countryside. You'll also see hut circles and burial chambers and an Iron Age fort at Castell Henllys or go fishing and pony trekking nearby. A visit to the Teifi Marshes Nature Reserve is a must for wildlife lovers.

Accommodation: 28 beds: 2x2-, 3x4- and 2x6-bed rooms.

8.00-10.00am
5.00-10.30pm

Pen-y-Pass B

Pen-y-Pass, Nantgwynant, Caernarfon, Gwynedd LL55 4NY
Tel: 0870 770 5990

Pen-y-Pass sits more than 1,000ft above sea level on Snowdon's famous Pyg Track, so gives you a decent head start for an ascent to the summit. The property has been the haunt of climbers and mountaineers for more than a century and even George Mallory of Everest-scaling fame stayed here on his early trips to Wales. Mountains lie in every direction but for those not interested in climbing, there are museums, railways, gardens and the North Wales coastline a short distance away. Home-cooked meals are served here and breakfast is included in the price. Limited parking.

Accommodation: 79 beds: a few 2-, mostly 4-6-bed - some en-suite.

7.00am -
10.30pm

Poppit Sands C

Sea View, Poppit, Cardigan, Pembrokeshire SA43 3LP
Tel: 0870 770 5996

Set in five acres of grounds stretching down to the sea, this popular property overlooks a fantastic Blue Flag beach popular with dolphins and seals as well as YHA's guests. Horse riding, cycle hire and fishing are all possible from here. You'll also find comfortable facilities, lovely sea views and easy access to the beach. For a day out, Cardigan is four miles away with its coastal farm park, Teifi Marshes Nature Reserve and shops for fresh supplies, as it's self-catering only here.

Accommodation: 34 beds: 2-, 4- and 6-bed rooms.

9.00-10.00am
5.00-10.30pm

For information and to book visit **www.yha.org.uk** or call **0870 770 8868**

Welsh Mountains, Moorland and Coastline

Port Eynon

Old Lifeboat House, Port Eynon, Swansea SA3 1NN
Tel: 0870 770 5998

The Gower Peninsula in South Wales was the first place to be designated an Area of Outstanding Natural Beauty and it is easy to see why. We occupy a former lifeboat station on an award-winning beach that is as popular with watersports enthusiasts as it is with families. The nearby Gower Coastal Walk covers 34 miles of heritage coast. YHA Port Eynon is self-catering only but you'll find a general store, fish and chip shop and a pub nearby.

Accommodation: 28 beds: 3x2-, 2x4-, 1x6- and 1x8-bed rooms.

8.00-10.00am
5.00-9.00pm

Pwll Deri

Castell Mawr, Trefasser, Goodwick, Pembrokeshire SA64 0LR
Tel: 0870 770 6004

In a remote and idyllic cliff-top setting, this simple self-catering cottage has spectacular views and enjoys glorious sunsets. The Pembrokeshire Coast Path runs past the front door and you can follow it north to Strumble Head, with its bird hide and spectacular lighthouse or south to the beaches at Pwllcrochan and Aber Mawr. The busy port at Fishguard, with ferries and catarmarans to Ireland, is just three miles east of here and is handy for supplies as this cottage is extremely isolated.

Accommodation: 31 beds: 2x2-, 1x4-, 1x7- and 2x8-bed rooms.

8.30-10.00am
5.00-10.30pm

Rowen

Rhiw Farm, Rowen, Conwy LL32 8YW
Tel: 0870 770 6012

The pretty village of Rowen sits above the Conwy Valley and is an ideal base to explore the hills and mountains inland and the bustling north Wales coastline. All the charm and character you'd expect to find in a traditional Welsh farmhouse comes complete with fabulous views. You'll discover burial chambers, standing stones, a Roman fort, a rare breeds farm and a good selection of pubs and restaurants close by. It's self-catering only so stock up before heading up the mile of narrow track.

Accommodation: 24 beds: 1x2-, 1x4-, 1x8- and 1x10-bed rooms.

8.00-10.00am
5.00-10.00pm

Welsh Mountains, Moorland and Coastline

Snowdon Ranger E

Rhyd Ddu, Caernarfon, Gwynedd LL54 7YS
Tel: 0870 770 6038

Most people staying here attempt the 3,560 ft ascent up Wales' highest mountain straight from our front door. On clear days, Ireland, Northern Ireland, Scotland, England and Wales are all visible. In summer, they cool off with a swim in the lake from our own beach and in winter, relax by the fire in this homely former inn and tuck into hearty home-cooked meals in our restaurant. Loads more hills are close by plus Beddgelert, Sygun Copper Mine and Caernarfon Castle.

Accommodation: 59 beds: mostly 2- and 4-bed rooms.

7.30-10.00am
5.00-11.00pm

St David's — Granary (Hostel) ★★ Dairy (Bunkhouse) ★★★★  F

Llaethdy, Whitesands, St David's, Pembrokeshire SA62 6PR
Tel: 0870 770 6042

St David's is Britain's smallest city and set in the middle of rural, coastal Pembrokeshire, it's a most unlikely location for a spectacular cathedral. Recently refurbished, the four star dairy bunkhouse is a conversion of a farmhouse and outbuildings near Whitesands Bay, one of the most beautiful beaches in the county. Families and surfers love it, as do birdwatchers who visit the RSPB reserve on nearby Ramsay Island. There are water sports centres and an Oceanarium in St David's.

Accommodation: 30 beds: 1x8-, 2x4-, 5x2- bedrooms, plus 1x4-bed self-contained flat in separate building.

8.00-10.00am
5.00-10.00pm

Fron Haul — A

Fron Haul Guesthouse, Sodom, Bodfari, Denbighshire LL16 4DY. Tel: 01745 710301

Fron Haul is a charming and unusual house in Bodfari, close to the hills and mountains of the Clwydian Range in the heart of beautiful north Welsh countryside. Built in the last century by a wealthy surgeon, the property offers superb views. Bodfari is close to Offa's Dyke and the Welsh seaside towns of Rhyll and Prestatyn are a short distance away. The picturesque and historic market town of Denbigh is also close and the Afonwen Craft and Antique Centre in the Clwydian Hills is also worth a visit.

Accommodation: 6 beds: 3x2-bed rooms.

Little Brompton Farm ◆◆◆◆ A

Montgomery , SY15 6HY
Tel: 01686 668371

This 17th Century farmhouse B&B forms part of a working farm two miles from the Georgian town of Montgomery in Powys. Right on the Offa's Dyke footpath, it is a warm and friendly place to relax. If it's too wet to walk, visit the lovely town of Welshpool with its Llanfair Railway and impressive Powis Castle or Newtown on the River Severn has a good textile museum. Local produce is used as much as possible in the dining room and luggage transport can be arranged for walkers. Open all year.

Accommodation: 6 beds: 1 double, 1 twin and 1 family room.

For information and to book visit **www.yha.org.uk** or call **0870 770 8868**

Welsh Mountains, Moorland and Coastline

Severn Farm | A

Severn Farm B&B, Welshpool, Powys, SY21 7BB
Tel: 01938 555999

An award-winning B&B in a modernised farmhouse with excellent facilities and a relaxing atmosphere. Located close to the town and ideal for discovering the area known as the 'gateway to Wales'.

Accommodation: 10: 3x2- and 1x4- bedded rooms.

Riverside | ★ ★ | A

Cinderhill Street, Monmouth, NP25 5EY
Tel: 01600 715577

The privately-owned Riverside Hotel offers guests a warm welcome and a high standard of accommodation. Originally a 19th Century coaching inn, the building is set in a quiet corner of historic Monmouth, ideal for both business and leisure travellers.

Accommodation: 34 beds: 6 doubles, 11 twins.

Dolgoch | F

Dolgoch, Tregaron, Ceredigion SY25 6NR
Tel: 0870 770 8868

Head into the wilds to this remote, gas-lit farmhouse in the lovely Tywi Valley for an experience to remember. There is no electricity so take a torch, and the only heating is an open fire. You'll have to make your own entertainment, but with excellent birdwatching and walking country all around, you won't have trouble keeping yourself busy. The Welsh National Cycle Route runs nearby.

Gower | A

Borfa House Activity Centre, Port Eynon, Swansea SA3 1NN. Tel: 01792 401548

A Victorian village house providing a high standard of accommodation situated next to a sandy beach. On the Gower Peninsula, Britain's first Area of Outstanding Natural Beauty, this is an ideal base for you to explore the coves, woods and moorland on the doorstep as well as the Heritage Centre and Gower's castles. Activity packages for surfing, climbing, kayaking and more.

Llangattock Mountain | A

Wern Whatkin, Hillside, Langattock, Crickhowell, NP8 1LG. Tel: 01873 812307

This mountain-top bunkhouse makes an ideal base for an 'away from it all' break. It's ideally situated for exploring local ancient woodlands, rare marshland and wildflower meadows. Llangattock caves, cliffs, mountain walks and Blaenavon World Heritage Site are all within walking distance.

Rhossili | A

Rhossili Activity Centre, Middleton, Rhossili, Swansea SA3 1PJ. Tel: 01792 401548

Originally the Victorian village schoolhouse, now refurbished with modern facilities to provide an excellent base to explore the Gower Peninsula and take advantage of one of Britain's best-known surfing beaches. On the edge of Rhossili Down it's a good base for any outdoor enthusiast, with all inclusive packages for surfing, climbing, kayaking and more.

GUESTHOUSE

BUNKHOUSE

BUNKHOUSE

Welsh Mountains, Moorland and Coastline

Swansea

Dan-y-Coed House, Huntington Close, West Cross, Swansea SA3 5AL. Tel: 01792 401548

A grand Victorian house on the outskirts of Mumbles village with the Gower Peninsula just around the headland and a four mile sandy beach just two minutes walk away. Visit the Dylan Thomas Centre, Oystermouth Castle, any of Swansea's theatre and music venues or just relax in the garden. Take advantage of the many sporting activities available, including watersports and horse riding or walk the hills, woods and moors of the Gower.

59 🛏	TV	🌳	Ⓟ	🍽					8.30am - 5.00pm

Tyncornel

Llanddewi-Brefi, Tregaron, Ceredigion SY25 6PH Tel: 0870 770 8868

The recent introduction of electricity to this bunkhouse has done nothing to detract from the true sense of wilderness and isolation on offer here. Red kites, buzzards and ravens fly above this simply furnished property, seven miles from the nearest phone box and a mile from the nearest house. A mile of unsurfaced road leads to YHA Tyncornel, popular with walkers, adventurous cyclists, bird watchers and those looking for total peace and solitude. The nearest pubs and shops are at Llanddewi-Brefi, seven miles and Tregaron 10 miles away.

16 🛏	Ⓟ	🍲							8.00-10.00am 5.00-10.00pm

For information and to book visit **www.yha.org.uk** or call **0870 770 8868**

Your help achieves so much

By donating regularly, you will help us maintain and improve our network of locations. Your gift will help future generations enjoy and experience YHA, and knowing your gift is due allows us to have more confidence in future planning. You can choose how you give, whether you give monthly or annually and how long you give for. It's a convenient, cost and tax effective way of giving.

Donation
HOTLINE
0800 652 4885

Q: Is YHA just for Young People?
A: YHA welcomes visitors of all ages.

Q: Do I have to share a room?
A: No, many locations have private rooms that you can have to yourself or share with your partner, friends or family.

Q: Do I have to do chores?
A: We have dedicated staff to make sure that the accommodation is clean. The only thing we ask is that you tidy up after yourselves.

Q: Do I have to bring my own bed linen?
A: No, laundered bed linen, pillows, duvet and blankets are provided. All you have to bring is a towel.

Q: What is there to do in the evenings?
A: Some of our locations are in towns and cities with bars, restaurants, theatres and night clubs. In our more rural locations there's always a selection of activities, from board games to kite making, keeping the children amused and giving you time to relax. For more organised entertainment, why not book an activity break at one of our activity centres (see page 111).

Q: Can I get into the accommodation during the day?
A: If you have already checked in you will have some access to the building. This access varies between properties. If you have booked a family room then you will have access to your room throughout the day. Please refer to the reception opening times.

Q: How do I find out about the area?
A: Our staff know their local areas well and will help you find the best activities making sure you get the most out of your stay.

Q: Can I hire the whole Youth Hostel?
A: Yes, you can hire some of our Youth Hostels under our Escape to... scheme (see page 10) visit our dedicated website: www.escape-to.co.uk.

Q: Can I bring a group?
A: Yes, we offer a wide choice for groups. YHA is perfect for groups of every age, from school children to adults. Our residential breaks and special packages offer exceptional value.

Q: Can I bring a school group?
A: Yes, all staff work to the most exacting standards in matters of health, safety and security. All our properties are fully risk assessed and YHA is also registered with the Criminal Records Bureau. Visit www.learn4real.co.uk for more information.

Q: Is there any financial support for school children who can't afford to join their classmates on a YHA trip?
A: Through our charity, Breaks4Kids, we are committed to providing disadvantaged children with the chance to experience YHA along with their class. To find out more, call 01629 592696 / www.yha-breaks4kids.org.uk

Q: Can I have my wedding at a YHA?
A: We have a small number of venues that are licensed to hold weddings but we can also offer something different

for a naming ceremony, blessing or any other special occasion.

Q: What facilities do you offer for children?
A: Many YHAs cater for families with children aged three years and under, offering cots, highchairs, towels, baby baths and baby alarm - ask for availability when you pre-book.

Q: Is there a catering service?
A: Many locations offer a full catering service from breakfast to picnic lunch and dinner. Some can also provide celebratory meals or functions for special occasions, and most have self-catering kitchens. See the individual entries for more information.

Q: Can I bring my own alcohol with me?
A: If you are staying in a licensed YHA, customers are not permitted to bring or consume their own alcohol. Alcohol can still be brought to non-licensed premises, and Escape to... Bookings (Please see conditions of hire).

Q: Can I bring my dog?
A: Only Registered Assistance Dogs are allowed in YHA's.

Q: Is my YHA Membership card valid overseas?
A: Your YHA membership card is also a Hostelling International membership card, which allows you to stay at Youth Hostels worldwide. If you are visiting England and Wales from abroad, you can either buy at home or international membership on arrival.

Q: Are YHA's open all year round?
A: Some of our larger properties are open all year round. Visit www.yha.org.uk or call 0870 770 8868 for more information.

Q: What security standards are in place?
A: YHA staff will do all they can to ensure your personal safety and the security of your belongings. Some YHAs provide secure lockers.

Q: My friends want to become members of YHA, can they join online?
A: Yes, they can join online at www.yha.org.uk or telephone: 0870 770 8868 with their credit/debit card details. They can also join at any of our YHA centres across England & Wales and selected agents & tourist information centres.

Q: How long does this Accommodation Guide last for?
A: This guide is valid from January 2007 to December 2008. During this time there may be changes to YHA's network - for up to date information visit the website at www.yha.org.uk or call 0870 770 8868.

It's easy to book

To check availability and make a booking visit www.yha.org.uk or phone the contact centre on 0870 770 8868

Youth Hostels by location

COAST

Stumble Head, Dyfed, Wales
britononview / Martin Brent

Anglesey Outdoors	123	Margate	47
Arnside	99	Marloes Sands	129
Bangor	123	Newport	130
Beer	27	Penzance	33
Boggle Hole	87	Perranporth	33
Borth	124	Poppit Sands	130
Boscastle Harbour	28	Port Eynon	131
Boswinger	28	Portland	34
Broad Haven	124	Pwll Deri	131
Conwy	126	Quantock Hills	34
Coverack	29	River Dart	34
Duddon Estuary	103	Salcombe	35
Golant	30	Sandown	48
Great Yarmouth	56	Scarborough	91
Hunstanton	56	Sheringham	58
Jersey	22	Swanage	37
King's Lynn	57	Tintagel	37
Land's End	31	Totland Bay	50
Littlehampton	46	Treyarnon Bay	37
Lizard Point	31	Truleigh Hill	50
Lulworth Cove	32	Wells-next-the-Sea	58
Lynton	32	Whitby	91
Manorbier	129		

CITY

Bath	27
Brighton	44
Bristol	28
Cambridge	55
Canterbury	44
Cardiff	126
Carlisle	101
Chester	101
Dover	45
Durham	115
Exeter	30
Liverpool	108
London Central	19
London Earls Court	19
London Holland Park	19
London Oxford Street	20
London St. Pancras	20
London St. Pauls	20
London Thameside	21
Manchester	108
Milton Keynes	47
Newcastle	116
Oxford	48
Stratford-upon-Avon	69
York	92
York Racecourse	92

COUNTRYSIDE

Alfriston	43	Epping Forest	56	Malham	90
Alston	99	Eskdale	104	Mankinholes	90
Alstonefield	75	Exford	30	Matlock	79
Ambleside	99	Eyam	77	Medway	47
Arundel	43	Ffynon Wen	127	Minehead	32
Bakewell	75	Gradbach Mill	77	National Forest	62
Bellever	27	Grasmere BH	105	Ninebanks	117
Betws-y-Coed	123	Grasmere TH	105	Okehampton	33
Beverley Friary	87	Grinton Lodge	87	Once Brewed	117
Birdoswald	100	Hartington Hall	78	Osmotherley	90
Black Sail	100	Hathersage	78	Patterdale	108
Blaxhall	55	Hawes	88	Pen-y-Pass	130
Borrowdale	100	Hawkshead	105	Ravenstor	79
Brecon	124	Haworth	88	Rowen	131
Bretton	75	Helmsley	88	Saffron Walden	57
Bridges Long Mynd	67	Helvellyn	106	Salisbury	35
Brighstone	43	Hindhead	45	Sherwood Forest	62
Bryn Gywnant	125	Holmbury St Mary	45	Shining Cliff	80
Burley	44	Honister Hause	106	Slaidburn	109
Buttermere	101	Idwal Cottage	127	Slimbridge	35
Byrness	115	Ilam Hall	78	Snowdon Ranger	132
Capel Curig	125	Ingleton	89	St Briavels Castle	36
Capel-y-Ffin	125	Ivinghoe	46	St Davids	132
Castle Hedingham	55	Jordans	46	Stainforth	91
Castleton	76	Kendal	106	Stow-on-the-Wold	36
Cheddar	29	Keswick	107	Streatley-on-Thames	48
Cholderton	29	Kettlewell	89	Street	36
Clun Mill	67	Kielder	116	Tanners Hatch	49
Coalbrookdale	67	Kings	127	Telscombe	49
Coalport	68	Kington	68	The Ridgeway	49
Cockermouth	102	Lakeside	107	Thurlby	62
Coniston Coppermines	102	Langdale	107	Wastwater	109
Coniston Holly How	102	Langdon Beck	116	Welsh Bicknor	69
Crowden	76	Langsett	79	Wilderhope Manor	69
Danywenallt	126	Lee Valley	57	Windermere	109
Derwentwater	103	Leominster	68	Woody's Top	63
Dimmingsdale	76	Litton Cheney	31	Wooler	117
Dufton	103	Llanberis	128	Youlgreave	80
Edale	77	Llanddeusant	128		
Edmundbyers	115	Llangollen	128		
Elterwater	104	Llwyn-y-Celyn	129		
Ennerdale	104	Lockton	89		

YHA Accommodation index

Youth Hostels

Name	Page
A	
Alfriston	43
Alston	99
Alstonefield	75
Ambleside	99
Anglesey Outdoors	123
Arnside	99
Arundel	43
B	
Bakewell	75
Bangor	123
Bath	27
Beer	27
Bellever	27
Betws-y-Coed	123
Beverley	87
Birdoswald	100
Black Sail	100
Blaxhall	55
Boggle Hole	87
Borrowdale	100
Borth	124
Boscastle Harbour	28
Boswinger	28
Brecon	124
Bretton	75
Bridges Long Mynd	67
Brighstone	43
Brighton	44
Bristol	28
Broad Haven	124
Bryn Gwynant	125
Burley	44
Buttermere	101
Byrness	115
C	
Cambridge	55
Canterbury	44
Capel Curig	125
Capel-y-Ffin	125
Cardiff	126
Carlisle	101
Castle Hedingham	55
Castleton	76
Cheddar	29
Chester	101
Cholderton	29

Name	Page
Clun Mill	67
Coalbrookedale	67
Coalport	68
Cockermouth	102
Coniston	
Coppermines	102
Coniston Holly How	102
Conwy	126
Coverack	29
Crowden	76
D	
Danywenallt	126
Derwentwater	103
Dimmingsdale	76
Dover	45
Duddon Estuary	103
Dufton	103
Durham	115
E	
Edale	77
Edmundbyers	115
Elterwater	104
Ennerdale	104
Epping Forest	56
Eskdale	104
Exeter	30
Exford	30
Eyam	77
F	
Ffynnon Wen	127
G	
Golant	30
Gradbach	77
Grasmere Butharlyp How	105
Grasmere Thorney How	105
Great Yarmouth	56
Grinton	87
H	
Hartington Hall	78
Hathersage	78
Hawes	88
Hawkshead	105
Haworth	88

Name	Page
Helmsley	88
Helvellyn	106
Hindhead	45
Holmbury St Mary	45
Honister Hause	106
Hunstanton	56
I	
Idwal Cottage	127
Ilam	78
Ingleton	89
Ivinghoe	46
J	
Jersey	22
Jordans	46
K	
Kendal	106
Keswick	107
Kettlewell	89
Kielder	116
Kings	127
King's Lynn	57
Kington	68
L	
Lakeside	107
Lands End	31
Langdale	107
Langdon Beck	116
Langsett	79
Lee Valley	57
Leominster	68
Littlehampton	46
Litton Cheney	31
Liverpool	108
Lizard Point	31
Llanberis	128
Llanddeusant	128
Llangollen	128
Llwyn-y-Celyn	129
Lockton	89
London Central	19
London Earls Court	19
London Holland Park	19
London Oxford Street	20
London St. Pancras	20
London St. Pauls	20
London Thameside	21

Name	Page
Lulworth Cove	32
Lynton	32
M	
Malham	90
Manchester	108
Mankinholes	90
Manorbier	129
Margate	47
Marloes Sands	129
Matlock	79
Medway	47
Milton Keynes	47
Minehead	32
N	
National Forest	62
Newcastle	116
Newport	130
Ninebanks	117
O	
Okehampton	33
Once Brewed	117
Osmotherley	90
Oxford	48
P	
Patterdale	108
Pen-y-Pass	130
Penzance	33
Perranporth	33
Poppit Sands	130
Port Eynon	131
Portland	34
Pwll Deri	131
Q	
Quantock Hills	34
R	
Ravenstor	79
River Dart	34
Rowen	131
S	
Saffron Walden	57
Salcombe	39
Salisbury	39

YHA Accommodation index

Youth Hostels

Name	Page
Sandown	48
Scarborough	91
Sheringham	58
Sherwood Forest	62
Shining Cliff	80
Slaidburn	109
Slimbridge	35
Snowdon Ranger	132
St Briavels Castle	36
St Davids	132
Stainforth	
Stow on the Wold	36
Stratford-upon-Avon	69
Streatley-on-Thames	48
Street	36
Swanage	37

T

Name	Page
Tanners Hatch	49
Telscombe	49
The Ridgeway	49
Thurlby	62
Tintagel	37
Totland Bay	50
Treyarnon Bay	37
Truleigh Hill	50

W

Name	Page
Wastwater	109
Wells-next-the Sea	58
Welsh Bicknor	69
Whitby	91
Wilderhope Manor	69
Windermere	109
Woody's Top	63
Wooler	117

Y

Name	Page
York	92
York Racecourse	92
Youlgreave	80

Guest houses

Name	Page
F	
Fron Haul	132
L	
Little Brompton Farm	132
M	
Magnolia Bishops Castle	70
O	
Oxford Cottage	70
R	
Redhurst B&B	63
Riverside Hotel	133
S	
Severn Farm	133

Bunkhouses

Name	Page
A	
All Stretton	70
B	
Bishopdale	92
C	
Clyffe Pypard	38
D	
Dolgoch	133
G	
Gower	133
Grindon	118
L	
Llangattock Mountain	133

Bunkhouses

Name	Page
P	
Portreath	38
R	
Rhossili	133
S	
Sheen	80
Swansea	134
Stour Valley	58
T	
Tyncornel	134

Camping Barns

Name	Page
A	
Abney	81
Alstonefield	81
B	
Bankshead	110
Barrasford	118
Birchover	81
Brompton On Swale	93
Butterton A	81
Butterton B	81
C	
Chenson	38
Chipping	110
Cold Blow	50
D	
Downham	110
E	
Edale	81
F	
Farndale	93
G	
Great Hound Tor	38

Camping Barns

Name	Page
H	
High Gillerthwaite	110
Holwick	118
K	
Kildale	93
L	
Lopwell	38
Lovesome Hill	93
Low Row	93
Lydford	38
M	
Middleton-by-Youlgreave	82
Mullacott Farm	39
N	
Nab End	82
Northcombe	39
P	
Puttenham	50
R	
Richmond	93
Runnage	39
S	
Sinnington	94
T	
Taddington	82
Trawden	110
U	
Underbank	82
W	
Wearhead	118
Westerdale	94
Witton	118
Woodadvent	39

It's easy to book

visit www.yha.org.uk or phone the contact centre on 0870 770 8868

'To help all, especially young people of limited means, to a greater knowledge, love and care of the countryside, and appreciation of the cultural values of towns and cities, particularly by providing Youth Hostels or other accommodation for them in their travels, and thus to promote their health, recreation and education'.

All information correct at time of going to print November 2006.
Printed on paper sourced from sustainable forests.

YHA Communications, Trevelyan House, Dimple Road, Matlock, Derbyshire DE4 3YH
Registered Charity No. 306122.

ISBN 978-0-904530-29-2